Atlas Instructions

The Atlas is phased upon the time of high water at Cherbourg. The predicted height of high water at Cherbourg is used to indicate the magnitude of each oscillation. Cherbourg has been specially selected as a reference port because it has a range suitable for tabulation and is relatively free from fluctuations in mean sea level which are prevalent at Dover and elsewhere. A bookmark is supplied with the Atlas which gives the times and heights of H.W.Cherbourg and this bookmark can be renewed in the Spring of each year by sending the old bookmark and a stamped and addressed envelope to the publishers. Alternatively the official French tide table is contained in a pamphlet available from J.D.Potter Ltd, Chart Agents, 145 Minories, London EC3. Cherbourg tide tables are also included in the popular almanacs.

TIME

The tide tables used will usually be for 'Time Zone -0100' or 'Temps Universal + 1 heure' (which are the same) but this should be checked carefully. Some French tables are expressed in local time which could be two hours ahead of GMT. At present British Summer time (BST) is one hour ahead of GMT and is therefore the same as is used by the French for their official Cherbourg tide tables. Since most cruising takes place during the summer months, it is suggested that ships' clocks be kept to British Summer Time, irrespective of times which may be kept on the continent. The following adjustments will then apply:

1   If the tide tables used are for 'Time Zone 0100' or 'Temps Universal + 1 heure', in Summer with ships' clocks and watches set to BST use the times as shown in the tables without adjustment. In Winter with ships' clocks and watches set to local British time (which will be GMT) subtract 1 hour from the times shown in the tide tables.

2   If the tide tables are expressed in Greenwich Mean Time (GMT), in Summer with ships' clocks and watches set to BST, add 1 hour to the times shown in the tide tables. In Winter with ships' clocks and watches set to local British time (which will be GMT) use the tide tables without adjustment.

Note   It is possible as a temporary expedient to use Dover tide tables, though accuracy will be impaired. H.W.Dover is approximately 3 hours and 15 minutes after H.W.Cherbourg, and this must be subtracted from the Dover time to give the approximate time of H.W.Cherbourg. The resultant time will be in GMT,

since Dover predictions are almost always given in GMT, and it will be necessary to apply the time in Summer and Winter as outlined in (2) above. The height of H.W.Dover is usually about 0.4 metres higher than at Cherbourg, and this must be subtracted from the Dover prediction.

PROCEDURE BEFORE SAILING

The following procedure should be followed before sailing so that information is obtained not only for planning the passage, but also is immediately available while on passage:

1   From the Cherbourg tide tables extract the time of H.W. for the required passage (inset A). Enter this time in pencil in the space provided on the H.W. page spread (top left) of the Atlas. Take care to establish the correct time of H.W.Cherbourg relative to ships' clocks and watches as already described.

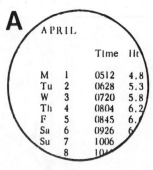

A

APRIL		Time	Ht
M	1	0512	4.8
Tu	2	0628	5.3
W	3	0720	5.8
Th	4	0804	6.2
F	5	0845	6.
Sa	6	0926	6
Su	7	1006	
	8	104	

This is a portion of a typical tide table giving times and heights of High Water at Cherbourg. For the examples in these instructions the time and height at Cherbourg for the morning of 2nd April are used, from which we note that H.W.Cherbourg is at 0628 hours, and the height is 5.3 metres.

2   Having entered the time of H.W.Cherbourg in the space provided, turn back page by page, entering the appropriate times in all the time spaces to '6 hours before H.W.Cherbourg'. Then make the appropriate entries, turning forward page by page from H.W.Cherbourg to '6 hours after H.W. Cherbourg (inset B).

3   If a passage is expected to extend beyond a tidal cycle, the H.W.Cherbourg prediction for the next following should also be entered in a like manner, and a second entry made on each page as described above. In these circumstances, and to avoid possible confusion, a note of the date may be added.

4   Extract fom the Cherbourg tide tables the height of H.W.Cherbourg which is to be found alongside the tidal times used (inset A).

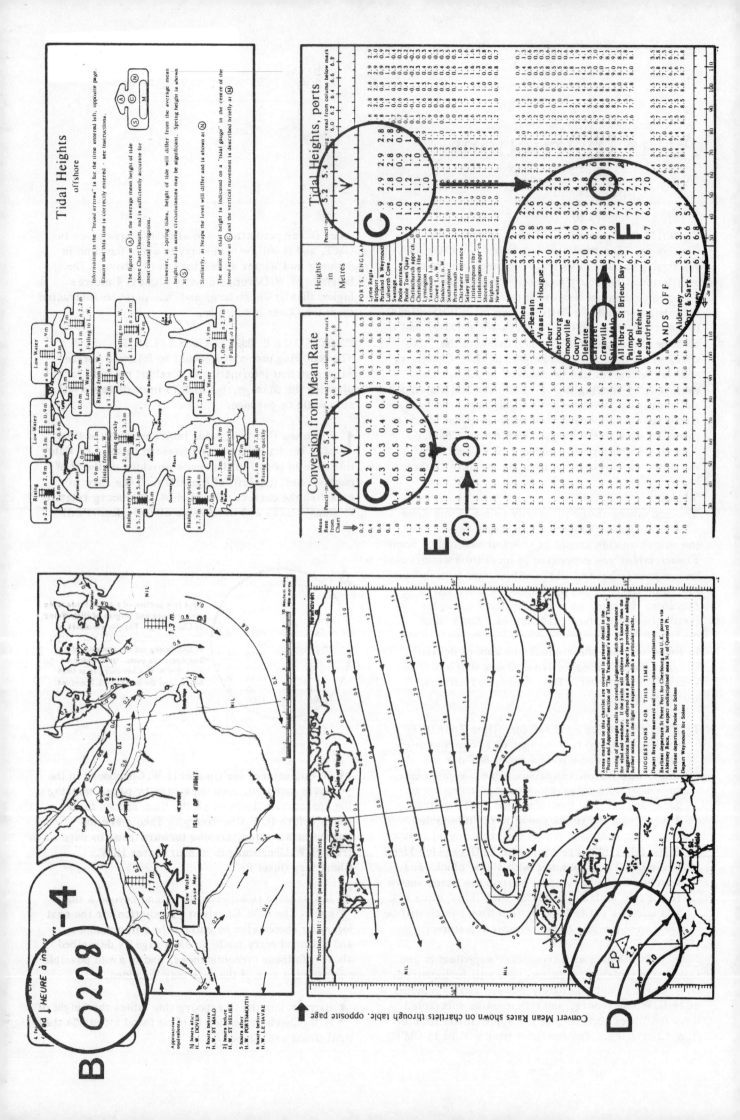

MICHAEL REEVE-FOWKES

The Yachtsman's TIDAL ATLAS

The SOLENT and CENTRAL CHANNEL

Lyme Regis and Lezardrieux to Newhaven and Le Havre

WITH CHARTLETS AND TABLES PROVIDING

'INSTANT' TIDAL STREAM RATES AND

'INSTANT' TIDAL HEIGHTS FOR

SOME SIXTY PORTS

AND PLACES

FLINT HALL PUBLICATIONS

The Solent Atlas first appeared in 'The Yachtsman's Manual of Tides' published
in 1983 and a Central Channel Atlas similar to that contained herein, but now
revised and updated, was first published by Stanford Maritime Ltd in 1977. For
these works the author studied data contained in the tide tables, stream atlases,
pilots and charts published by the Hydrographer of the Navy, the Service Hydro-
graphique et Oceanographique de la Marine, Paris, and the Chef der Hydrographie,
Holland, and gratefully acknowledges the great benefit he gained from these
publications. Further information was obtained from a variety of sources
including club rule books, cruising handbooks, articles in magazines, from the
author's own experience and that of many friends. However, it has to be said
that information from these various sources was from time to time conflicting
and often incomplete. The author therefore found it necessary when this occurred
to make assumptions based upon his best judgement, in the belief that such
assumptions made at desk and drawing board were likely to be better than those
which might otherwise have to be made at sea, perhaps under difficult conditions.
This study is offered as an aid to accurate navigation, but the author disclaims
all liability for any error or omission which may be present.

The author gratefully acknowledges the help of John Reeve-Fowkes for editing
the entire work and for the cover design and layout of this book.

First published 1985

© Michael Reeve-Fowkes 1985

Published, printed and bound by
Flint Hall Publications
12 Church Street, Eastbourne
Sussex

ISBN 0 946370 04 4

5 Opposite the chartlets on each page spread there are tables which provide the means of conversion of Mean Rates of stream shown on the chartlets to the rate of stream for a particular tide and for obtaining heights of tide at the listed ports and places. At the top of these tables are scales showing sundry heights of H.W.Cherbourg. Using the height obtained (see 4 above) put a vertical arrow (or other suitable mark) in pencil on the scales at the corresponding H.W. height and repeat on the scales throughout the Atlas (inset C). This arrow will indicate the correct vertical coloumn of figures to be used. Should the arrow fall between two vertical columns it will be necessary to interpolate between the figures in each column.

There is another scale at the bottom of each table headed 'Coefficient de la Marée' and this scale may be used instead of the H.W.Cherbourg scale by those who have acquired the necessary tables. The results will be very much the same, any difference reflecting the greater accuracy of the coefficient system. Tables of coefficients will be found in the pamphlet of Cherbourg tide tables mentioned above.

TO OBTAIN THE DIRECTION AND RATE OF A TIDAL STREAM

Turn to the page on which the pencilled time in the time box is nearest to ship's time, or if at the passage planning stage, refer to the pages appropriate to the planned passage. Marking the estimated position or fix on the stream chartlet, seek the nearest arrow or flowline. It is this one, or perhaps the interpolation of two, which is the key to the direction of the stream (inset D). Using a protractor or other suitable instrument, measure this direction against the magnetic meridian (the sloping line on all the chartlets) to determine the direction of the stream relative to Magnetic North. If working relative to True North, then measure the direction of the stream against the vertical side of the chartlet.

To obtain the rate of the stream, note the Mean Rate shown against the arrow or flowline nearest to the position, if necessary interpolating against neighbouring figures (inset D). The adjacent Conversion Table is then entered from the lefthand side with this Mean Rate and, following across the table to the column over which the pencilled arrow has been drawn, the rate of the tidal stream is extracted (inset E). Interpolation between two columns may be necessary. The rate is given in knots.

The process of tidal chartwork is explained in greater detail in 'The Yachtsman's Manual of Tides' and a useful practical method of transferring tidal stream directions from the tidal atlas to the passage chart is to be found in 'The Yachtsman's Log Book', both published by Flint Hall Publications.

TO FIND THE HEIGHT OF TIDE AT ANY OF THE LISTED PORTS AND PLACES

To find the height of tide at a port or place, turn to the page where the pencilled time is nearest to ship's time, or that page nearest the time for which information is required - for instance, an estimated time of arrival. Then enter the Tidal Height table with the port or place for which the information is required, follow across to the column above which the pencil mark has been made, and extract the tidal height

(inset F). If the pencil mark falls between two columns, interpolate between the two.

If the tidal height is required for a precise time, find the height figures as described above from two successive pages, and interpolate between the figures extracted.

All the tidal heights in the tables are for heights above chart datum (except obsolete fathoms charts) and may be applied to calculations as extracted. They must be added to chart soundings to obtain the total depth of water, and they must be subtracted from echo-sounder or leadline readings before they can be related to chart soundings.

All the double-page spreads contain information about tidal heights offshore, and it should be noted that these heights are quite closely related to the heights at ports and places nearby. Note also that the state of tide is briefly described - for example, 'Rising from L.W.', 'High Water' and 'Falling quickly'. If, therefore, it is desired to know the time of high water at any particular place, then the first step is to seek out the page where the offshore information indicates High Water. It is then possible to refer to the adjacent table of Tidal Heights at Ports and Places and compare the height extracted with those shown in the tables on the preceding and succeeding pages, and thus by interpolation determine whether high water at that place coincides with the time of high water offshore, or is before or after that time.

Note

On the tidal chartlets there are areas marked which refer to the 'Ports and Approaches' section of 'The Yachtsman's Manual of Tides'. This section contains large-scale tidal chartlets of the Solent and Approaches, Portland Bill, Alderney and Cherbourg, Poole, Russel Channels, St Helier Approaches, St Malo Approaches, Ile de Brehat, Le Havre, the Scilly Islands, Ile d'Ouessant and Chenal du Four. The Manual is published by Flint Hall Publications and is available from chandlers and booksellers.

Cross-Channel Passages

PASSAGE PLANNING IN TIDAL WATERS

In tidal waters it is the practice of merchant mariners to draw a suitable line on the chart along the intended course, making sure that there is sufficient depth of water and that no wrecks or dangers exist along it; then to steer following precisely this line, making necessary course adjustments from time to time to compensate for the effect of tidal streams, currents and leeway. These merchant mariners have handed down to many yachtsmen their navigational principle of following a track drawn across a tidal stream by periodic alterations of course, as illustrated in

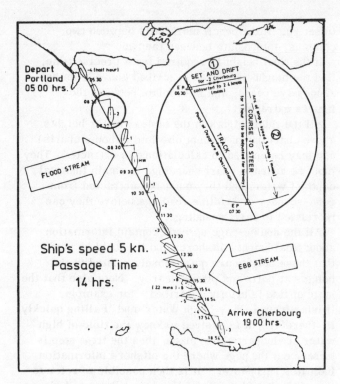

Fig. 1   Course setting to follow the track, involving much course alteration and resulting in a passage which will be longer than necessary.

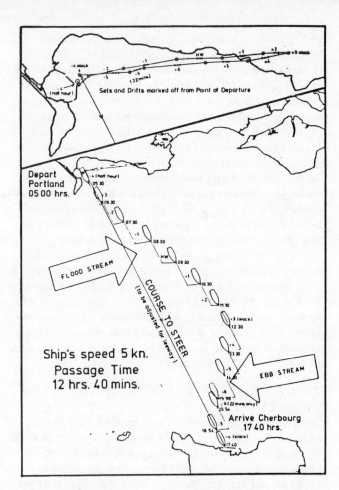

Fig. 2   Course planning, where the shortest distance between point of departure and destination is not the track, even though the course to steer is the same as the track.

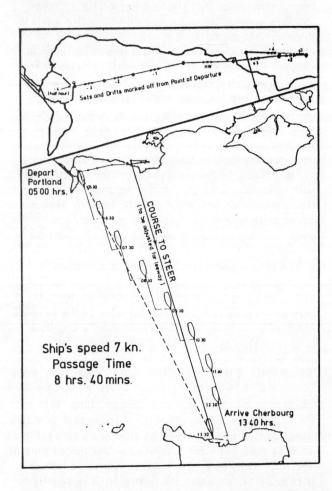

Fig. 3   Course planning, where the yacht achieving 7 knots steers a course quite different from the track, yet makes the fastest possible passage.

Figure 1. It is, of course, important that yachtsmen understand the simple geometry of this course-setting process to combat a stream because many short passages demand it; and indeed, for longer passages such as in the Thames Estuary cluttered with banks, or in the Channel Islands cluttered with rocks, it is often necessary to sail along a track drawn from one point to another in order to avoid these dangers. But for a passage across the Channel such as that illustrated in Figure 1 it is doubtful whether any case can be made to support the method, which involves numerous changes of course and therefore much additional chartwork, and may create difficulties in laying all of the courses because the wind may prove adverse for some of them. However, the main disadvantage is that the passage takes longer than necessary.

The alternative method, illustrated in Figures 2 and 3, is essential for fast passages. It involves steering a straight course through the water while the water itself is ebbing and flowing, causing the track over the ground to be a very distinct curve.

ACCUMULATED SETS AND DRIFTS
Having decided upon the speed of the yacht, the probable duration of the passage and the most advantageous time to depart, the sets and drifts are marked off on the passage chart from the point of departure. This is done by referring to each relevant page of the tidal atlas to decide the set and drift for each hour of the passage. The edge of a sheet of paper laid along the line Portland/Cherbourg and marked off into the $12\frac{1}{2}$ hourly divisions representing the expected duration of a 5-knot passage (or into 9 divisions for a 7-knot passage) will help to decide the anticipated position for each hour. Having plotted all the sets and drifts for the entire passage, the final plot will indicate the total effect of the tidal streams, and this plot is then joined to the point of destination, giving the course to steer.

Tidal Atlas

NOTES

Alderney Race   Passage through the race should if possible be avoided when wind-against-tide conditions prevail. On windless days passages south or southwest through the Alderney Race on the ebb stream will be comfortable. However, when heading north or northeast on the flood stream, small areas of turbulence occur as Alderney is approached and passed, coinciding with changes in depth of water. As a yacht passes north of a line Quenard Point/Cap de la Hague, this researcher has observed an area of undisciplined water not adequately recorded in pilots and journals, which extends 6 or 7 miles northwards into the English Channel during the period -2 to +1$\frac{1}{2}$ hours H.W.Cherbourg, and it is likely that the rate of flood stream in the area exceeds predictions. These uncomfortable conditions can be avoided if a passage is planned to pass through the area at slack water.

The Swinge and Ortac Channel   Race conditions with overfalls will prevail in these channels during both flood and ebb streams and it is therefore advisable to negotiate them at slack water.

Amphidromic Points   The main characteristic of an amphidromic point is that there is no predicted rise and fall of tide at that point. If co-tidal lines (that is, lines joining positions at which high water occurs at the same time) were to be drawn on the chart, then it would be found that they radiate from the amphidromic point, and that the lines rotate once in each tidal cycle around the point in an anti-clockwise direction. There are no true amphidromic points in the area covered by this atlas, but there is a tendency towards such a point in the area close to the west of the Isle of Wight. These places are known as false or degenerate amphidromic points and are characterised by small tidal ranges.

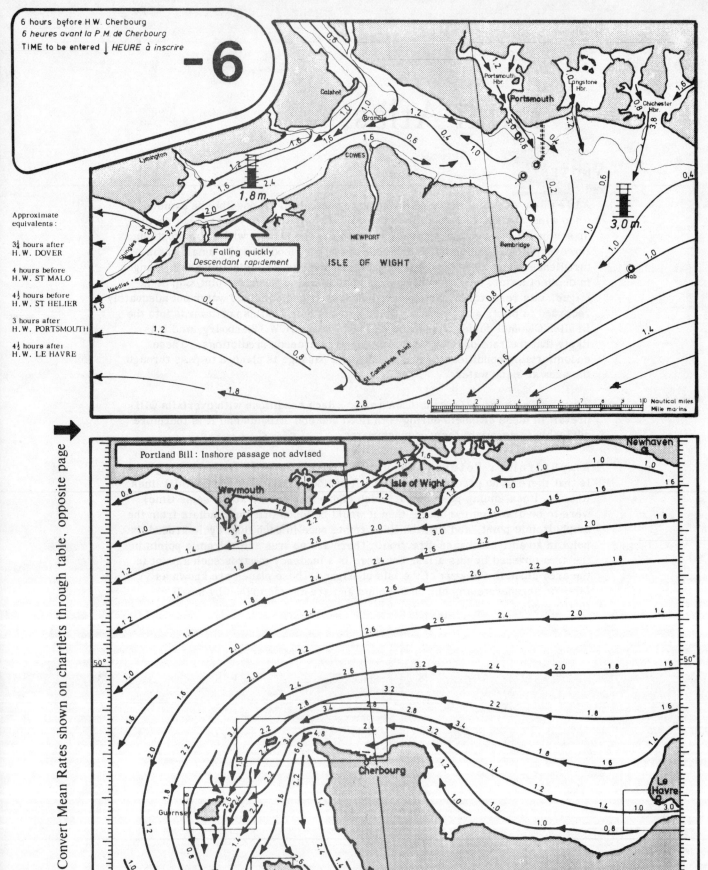

6 hours before H.W. Cherbourg
6 heures avant la P.M. de Cherbourg
TIME to be entered ↓ *HEURE à inscrire*

−6

Approximate
equivalents :

3¼ hours after
H.W. DOVER

4 hours before
H.W. ST MALO

4½ hours before
H.W. ST HELIER

3 hours after
H.W. PORTSMOUTH

4½ hours after
H.W. LE HAVRE

1,8 m.

Falling quickly
Descendant rapidement

3,0 m.

ISLE OF WIGHT

Lymington
Calshot
Bramble
COWES
NEWPORT
Bembridge
Needles
Shingles
St Catherines Point

Portsmouth Hbr.
Portsmouth
Langstone Hbr.
Chichester Hbr.
Nab

0 1 2 3 4 5 6 7 8 9 10 Nautical miles
Mille marins

Convert Mean Rates shown on chartlets through table, opposite page

Portland Bill : Inshore passage not advised

Weymouth
Isle of Wight
Newhaven

Guernsey
Cherbourg
Jersey
St. Malo
Le Havre

50°

49°

Areas marked on this chartlet are covered in greater detail in the
"Ports and Approaches" section of 'The Yachtsman's Manual of Tides''.

Timing of passages calls for careful judgement, with due allowance
for wind and weather. If the yacht will achieve about 5 knots, then the
suggestions below are offered as a guide. Space is provided for adding
further notes, in the light of experience with a particular yacht.

SUGGESTIONS FOR THIS TIME
Earliest departure Cherbourg for eastward destinations

....
....
....
....
....

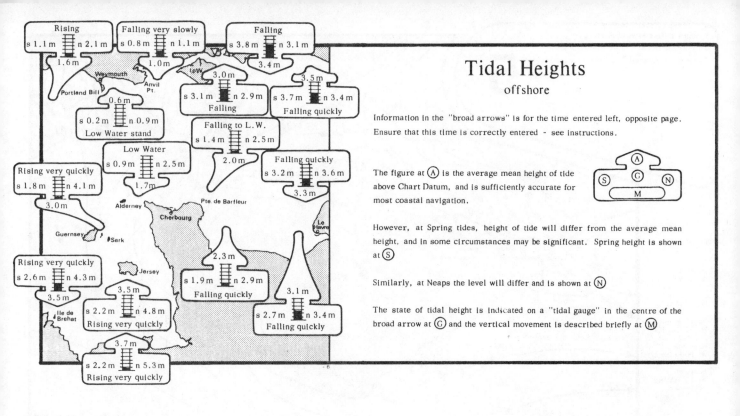

Tidal Heights
offshore

Information in the "broad arrows" is for the time entered left, opposite page. Ensure that this time is correctly entered - see instructions.

The figure at (A) is the average mean height of tide above Chart Datum, and is sufficiently accurate for most coastal navigation.

However, at Spring tides, height of tide will differ from the average mean height, and in some circumstances may be significant. Spring height is shown at (S)

Similarly, at Neaps the level will differ and is shown at (N)

The state of tidal height is indicated on a "tidal gauge" in the centre of the broad arrow at (G) and the vertical movement is described briefly at (M)

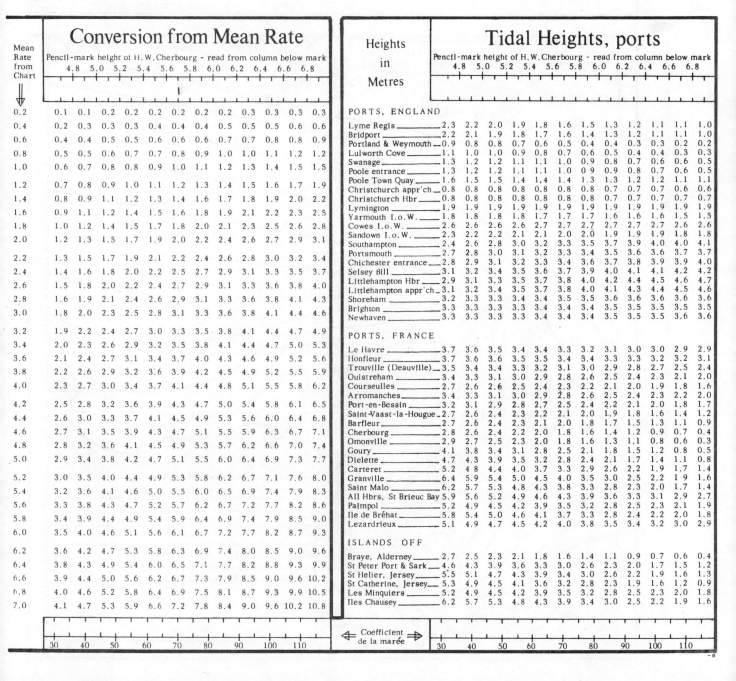

Conversion from Mean Rate

Mean Rate from Chart	Pencil-mark height of H.W. Cherbourg - read from column below mark										
	4.8	5.0	5.2	5.4	5.6	5.8	6.0	6.2	6.4	6.6	6.8
0.2	0.1	0.1	0.2	0.2	0.2	0.2	0.2	0.2	0.3	0.3	0.3	0.3
0.4	0.2	0.3	0.3	0.3	0.4	0.4	0.4	0.5	0.5	0.5	0.6	0.6
0.6	0.4	0.4	0.5	0.5	0.6	0.6	0.6	0.7	0.7	0.8	0.8	0.9
0.8	0.5	0.5	0.6	0.7	0.7	0.8	0.9	1.0	1.0	1.1	1.2	1.2
1.0	0.6	0.7	0.8	0.8	0.9	1.0	1.1	1.2	1.3	1.4	1.5	1.5
1.2	0.7	0.8	0.9	1.0	1.1	1.2	1.3	1.4	1.5	1.6	1.7	1.9
1.4	0.8	0.9	1.1	1.2	1.3	1.4	1.6	1.7	1.8	1.9	2.0	2.2
1.6	0.9	1.1	1.2	1.4	1.5	1.6	1.8	1.9	2.1	2.2	2.3	2.5
1.8	1.0	1.2	1.4	1.5	1.7	1.8	2.0	2.1	2.3	2.5	2.6	2.8
2.0	1.2	1.3	1.5	1.7	1.9	2.0	2.2	2.4	2.6	2.7	2.9	3.1
2.2	1.3	1.5	1.7	1.9	2.1	2.2	2.4	2.6	2.8	3.0	3.2	3.4
2.4	1.4	1.6	1.8	2.0	2.2	2.5	2.7	2.9	3.1	3.3	3.5	3.7
2.6	1.5	1.8	2.0	2.2	2.4	2.7	2.9	3.1	3.3	3.6	3.8	4.0
2.8	1.6	1.9	2.1	2.4	2.6	2.9	3.1	3.3	3.6	3.8	4.1	4.3
3.0	1.8	2.0	2.3	2.5	2.8	3.1	3.3	3.6	3.8	4.1	4.4	4.6
3.2	1.9	2.2	2.4	2.7	3.0	3.3	3.5	3.8	4.1	4.4	4.7	4.9
3.4	2.0	2.3	2.6	2.9	3.2	3.5	3.8	4.1	4.4	4.7	5.0	5.3
3.6	2.1	2.4	2.7	3.1	3.4	3.7	4.0	4.3	4.6	4.9	5.2	5.6
3.8	2.2	2.6	2.9	3.2	3.6	3.9	4.2	4.5	4.9	5.2	5.5	5.9
4.0	2.3	2.7	3.0	3.4	3.7	4.1	4.4	4.8	5.1	5.5	5.8	6.2
4.2	2.5	2.8	3.2	3.6	3.9	4.3	4.7	5.0	5.4	5.8	6.1	6.5
4.4	2.6	3.0	3.3	3.7	4.1	4.5	4.9	5.3	5.6	6.0	6.4	6.8
4.6	2.7	3.1	3.5	3.9	4.3	4.7	5.1	5.5	5.9	6.3	6.7	7.1
4.8	2.8	3.2	3.6	4.1	4.5	4.9	5.3	5.7	6.2	6.6	7.0	7.4
5.0	2.9	3.4	3.8	4.2	4.7	5.1	5.5	6.0	6.4	6.9	7.3	7.7
5.2	3.0	3.5	4.0	4.4	4.9	5.3	5.8	6.2	6.7	7.1	7.6	8.0
5.4	3.2	3.6	4.1	4.6	5.0	5.5	6.0	6.5	6.9	7.4	7.9	8.3
5.6	3.3	3.8	4.3	4.7	5.2	5.7	6.2	6.7	7.2	7.7	8.2	8.6
5.8	3.4	3.9	4.4	4.9	5.4	5.9	6.4	6.9	7.4	7.9	8.5	9.0
6.0	3.5	4.0	4.6	5.1	5.6	6.1	6.7	7.2	7.7	8.2	8.7	9.3
6.2	3.6	4.2	4.7	5.3	5.8	6.3	6.9	7.4	8.0	8.5	9.0	9.6
6.4	3.8	4.3	4.9	5.4	6.0	6.5	7.1	7.7	8.2	8.8	9.3	9.9
6.6	3.9	4.4	5.0	5.6	6.2	6.7	7.3	7.9	8.5	9.0	9.6	10.2
6.8	4.0	4.6	5.2	5.8	6.4	6.9	7.5	8.1	8.7	9.3	9.9	10.5
7.0	4.1	4.7	5.3	5.9	6.6	7.2	7.8	8.4	9.0	9.6	10.2	10.8

Scale: 30 40 50 60 70 80 90 100 110

Tidal Heights, ports

Heights in Metres

	Pencil-mark height of H.W. Cherbourg - read from column below mark										
	4.8	5.0	5.2	5.4	5.6	5.8	6.0	6.2	6.4	6.6	6.8
PORTS, ENGLAND											
Lyme Regis	2.3	2.2	2.0	1.9	1.8	1.6	1.5	1.3	1.2	1.1	1.1	1.0
Bridport	2.2	2.1	1.9	1.8	1.7	1.6	1.4	1.3	1.2	1.1	1.1	1.0
Portland & Weymouth	0.9	0.8	0.8	0.7	0.6	0.5	0.4	0.4	0.3	0.3	0.2	0.2
Lulworth Cove	1.1	1.0	1.0	0.9	0.8	0.7	0.6	0.5	0.4	0.4	0.3	0.3
Swanage	1.3	1.2	1.2	1.1	1.1	1.0	0.9	0.8	0.7	0.6	0.6	0.5
Poole entrance	1.3	1.2	1.2	1.1	1.1	1.0	0.9	0.9	0.8	0.7	0.6	0.5
Poole Town Quay	1.6	1.5	1.5	1.4	1.4	1.4	1.3	1.3	1.2	1.2	1.1	1.1
Christchurch appr'ch	0.8	0.8	0.8	0.8	0.8	0.8	0.8	0.7	0.7	0.7	0.6	0.6
Christchurch Hbr	0.8	0.8	0.8	0.8	0.8	0.8	0.8	0.7	0.7	0.7	0.7	0.7
Lymington	1.9	1.9	1.9	1.9	1.9	1.9	1.9	1.9	1.9	1.9	1.9	1.9
Yarmouth I.o.W.	1.8	1.8	1.8	1.8	1.7	1.7	1.7	1.6	1.6	1.6	1.5	1.5
Cowes I.o.W.	2.6	2.6	2.6	2.6	2.7	2.7	2.7	2.7	2.7	2.7	2.6	2.6
Sandown I.o.W.	2.3	2.2	2.2	2.1	2.1	2.0	2.0	1.9	1.9	1.9	1.8	1.8
Southampton	2.4	2.6	2.8	3.0	3.2	3.3	3.5	3.7	3.9	4.0	4.0	4.1
Portsmouth	2.7	2.8	3.0	3.1	3.2	3.3	3.4	3.5	3.6	3.6	3.7	3.7
Chichester entrance	2.8	2.9	3.1	3.2	3.3	3.4	3.6	3.7	3.8	3.9	3.9	4.0
Selsey Bill	3.1	3.2	3.4	3.5	3.6	3.7	3.9	4.0	4.1	4.1	4.2	4.2
Littlehampton Hbr	2.9	3.1	3.3	3.5	3.7	3.8	4.0	4.2	4.4	4.5	4.6	4.7
Littlehampton appr'ch	3.1	3.2	3.4	3.5	3.7	3.8	4.0	4.1	4.3	4.4	4.5	4.6
Shoreham	3.2	3.3	3.3	3.4	3.4	3.5	3.5	3.6	3.6	3.6	3.6	3.6
Brighton	3.3	3.3	3.3	3.3	3.4	3.4	3.4	3.5	3.5	3.5	3.5	3.5
Newhaven	3.3	3.3	3.3	3.3	3.4	3.4	3.4	3.5	3.5	3.5	3.6	3.6
PORTS, FRANCE											
Le Havre	3.7	3.6	3.5	3.4	3.4	3.3	3.2	3.1	3.0	3.0	2.9	2.9
Honfleur	3.7	3.6	3.6	3.5	3.5	3.4	3.4	3.3	3.3	3.2	3.2	3.1
Trouville (Deauville)	3.5	3.4	3.4	3.3	3.2	3.1	3.0	2.9	2.8	2.7	2.5	2.4
Ouistreham	3.4	3.3	3.1	3.0	2.9	2.8	2.6	2.5	2.4	2.3	2.1	2.0
Courseulles	2.7	2.6	2.6	2.5	2.4	2.3	2.2	2.1	2.0	1.9	1.8	1.6
Arromanches	3.4	3.3	3.1	3.0	2.9	2.8	2.6	2.5	2.4	2.3	2.2	2.0
Port-en-Bessin	3.2	3.1	2.9	2.8	2.7	2.5	2.4	2.2	2.1	2.0	1.8	1.7
Saint-Vaast-la-Hougue	2.7	2.6	2.4	2.3	2.2	2.1	2.0	1.9	1.8	1.6	1.4	1.2
Barfleur	2.7	2.6	2.4	2.3	2.1	2.0	1.8	1.7	1.5	1.3	1.1	0.9
Cherbourg	2.8	2.6	2.4	2.2	2.0	1.8	1.6	1.4	1.2	0.9	0.7	0.4
Omonville	2.9	2.7	2.5	2.3	2.0	1.8	1.6	1.3	1.1	0.8	0.6	0.3
Goury	4.1	3.8	3.4	3.1	2.8	2.5	2.1	1.8	1.5	1.2	0.8	0.5
Dielette	4.7	4.3	3.9	3.5	3.2	2.8	2.4	2.1	1.7	1.4	1.1	0.8
Carteret	5.2	4.8	4.4	4.0	3.7	3.3	2.9	2.6	2.2	1.9	1.7	1.4
Granville	6.4	5.9	5.4	5.0	4.5	4.0	3.5	3.0	2.5	2.2	19	1.6
Saint Malo	6.2	5.7	5.3	4.8	4.3	3.8	3.3	2.8	2.3	2.0	1.7	1.4
All Hbrs, St Brieuc Bay	5.9	5.6	5.2	4.9	4.6	4.3	3.9	3.6	3.3	3.1	2.9	2.7
Paimpol	5.2	4.9	4.5	4.2	3.9	3.5	3.2	2.8	2.5	2.3	2.1	1.9
Ile de Bréhat	5.8	5.4	5.0	4.6	4.1	3.7	3.3	2.8	2.4	2.2	2.0	1.8
Lezardrieux	5.1	4.9	4.7	4.5	4.2	4.0	3.8	3.5	3.4	3.2	3.0	2.9
ISLANDS OFF											
Braye, Alderney	2.7	2.5	2.3	2.1	1.8	1.6	1.4	1.1	0.9	0.7	0.6	0.4
St Peter Port & Sark	4.6	4.3	3.9	3.6	3.3	3.0	2.6	2.3	2.0	1.7	1.5	1.2
St Helier, Jersey	5.5	5.1	4.7	4.3	3.9	3.4	3.0	2.6	2.2	1.9	1.6	1.3
St Catherine, Jersey	5.3	4.9	4.5	4.1	3.6	3.2	2.8	2.3	1.9	1.6	1.2	0.9
Les Minquiers	5.3	4.9	4.5	4.2	3.9	3.5	3.2	2.8	2.5	2.3	2.0	1.8
Iles Chausey	6.2	5.7	5.3	4.8	4.3	3.9	3.4	3.0	2.5	2.2	1.9	1.6

⇐ Coefficient de la marée ⇒

Scale: 30 40 50 60 70 80 90 100 110

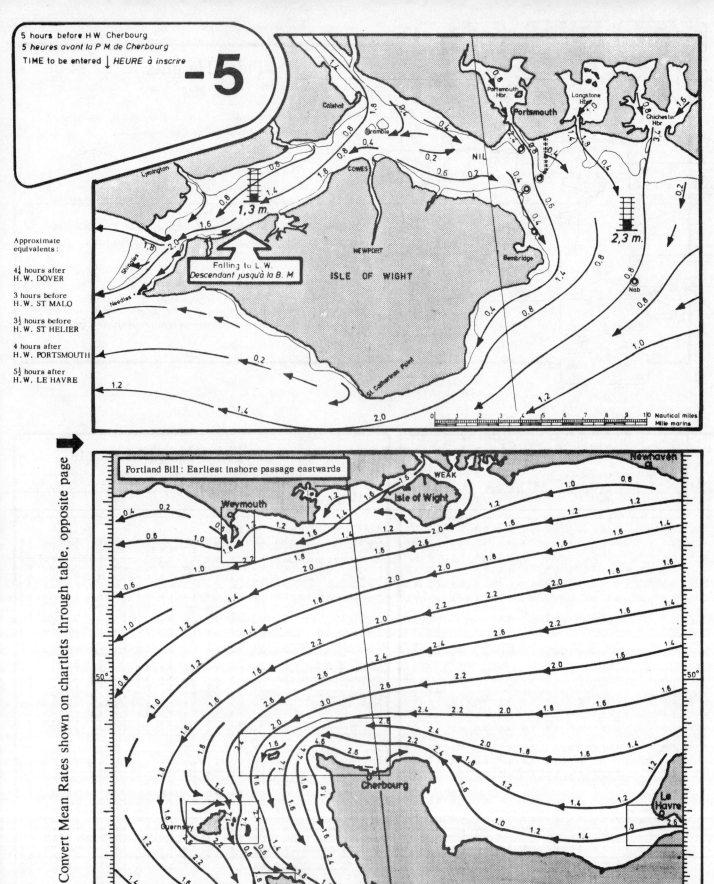

Approximate
equivalents :

4¼ hours after
H.W. DOVER

3 hours before
H.W. ST MALO

3½ hours before
H.W. ST HELIER

4 hours after
H.W. PORTSMOUTH

5½ hours after
H.W. LE HAVRE

1,3 m.

Falling to L.W.
Descendant jusqu'à la B.M.

ISLE OF WIGHT

2,3 m.

Portsmouth Hbr.
Portsmouth
Langstone Hbr.
Chichester Hbr.

Calshot
Bramble
COWES
NEWPORT
Lymington
Shingles
Needles
St Catherine's Point
Bembridge
Nab
NIL

0 1 2 3 4 5 6 7 8 9 10 Nautical miles
Mille marins

Convert Mean Rates shown on chartlets through table, opposite page

Portland Bill : Earliest inshore passage eastwards

Weymouth
Isle of Wight
WEAK
Newhaven

50°

Guernsey
Jersey
Cherbourg
Le Havre
St. Malo

49°

Areas marked on this chartlet are covered in greater detail in the
"Ports and Approaches" section of 'The Yachtsman's Manual of Tides".

Timing of passages calls for careful judgement, with due allowance
for wind and weather. If the yacht will achieve about 5 knots, then the
suggestions below are offered as a guide. Space is provided for adding
further notes, in the light of experience with a particular yacht.

SUGGESTIONS FOR THIS TIME

Depart Cherbourg for eastward destinations

Suggested departure St Malo for Granville

. . . .

. . . .

. . . .

. . . .

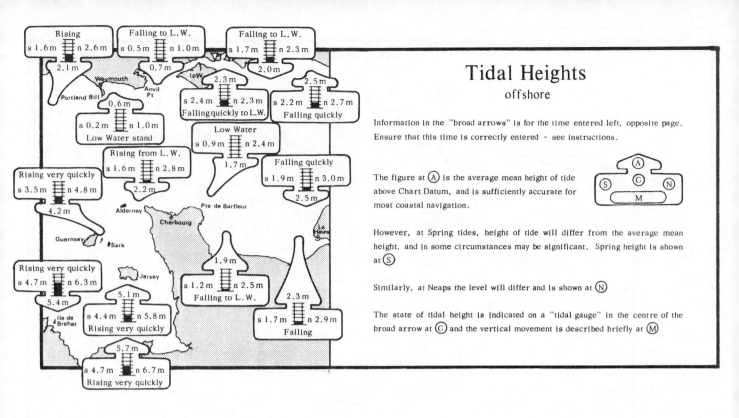

Tidal Heights
offshore

Information in the "broad arrows" is for the time entered left, opposite page. Ensure that this time is correctly entered - see instructions.

The figure at (A) is the average mean height of tide above Chart Datum, and is sufficiently accurate for most coastal navigation.

However, at Spring tides, height of tide will differ from the average mean height, and in some circumstances may be significant. Spring height is shown at (S)

Similarly, at Neaps the level will differ and is shown at (N)

The state of tidal height is indicated on a "tidal gauge" in the centre of the broad arrow at (G) and the vertical movement is described briefly at (M)

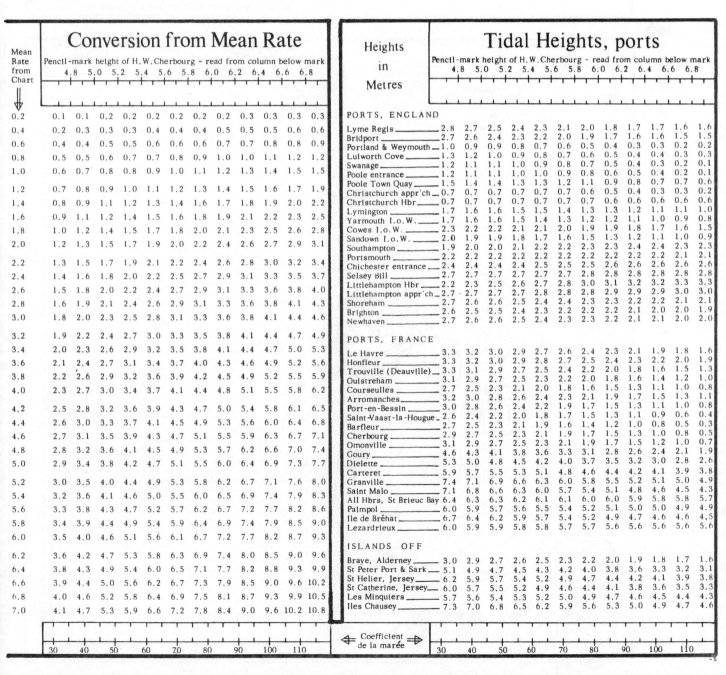

Conversion from Mean Rate

Pencil-mark height of H.W. Cherbourg - read from column below mark

Mean Rate from Chart	4.8	5.0	5.2	5.4	5.6	5.8	6.0	6.2	6.4	6.6	6.8	
0.2	0.1	0.1	0.2	0.2	0.2	0.2	0.2	0.2	0.2	0.3	0.3	0.3
0.4	0.2	0.3	0.3	0.3	0.4	0.4	0.4	0.5	0.5	0.5	0.6	0.6
0.6	0.4	0.4	0.5	0.5	0.6	0.6	0.6	0.7	0.7	0.8	0.8	0.9
0.8	0.5	0.5	0.6	0.7	0.7	0.8	0.9	1.0	1.0	1.1	1.2	1.2
1.0	0.6	0.7	0.8	0.8	0.9	1.0	1.1	1.2	1.3	1.4	1.5	1.5
1.2	0.7	0.8	0.9	1.0	1.1	1.2	1.3	1.4	1.5	1.6	1.7	1.9
1.4	0.8	0.9	1.1	1.2	1.3	1.4	1.6	1.7	1.8	1.9	2.0	2.2
1.6	0.9	1.1	1.2	1.4	1.5	1.6	1.8	1.9	2.1	2.2	2.3	2.5
1.8	1.0	1.2	1.4	1.5	1.7	1.8	2.0	2.1	2.3	2.5	2.6	2.8
2.0	1.2	1.3	1.5	1.7	1.9	2.0	2.2	2.4	2.6	2.7	2.9	3.1
2.2	1.3	1.5	1.7	1.9	2.1	2.2	2.4	2.6	2.8	3.0	3.2	3.4
2.4	1.4	1.6	1.8	2.0	2.2	2.5	2.7	2.9	3.1	3.3	3.5	3.7
2.6	1.5	1.8	2.0	2.2	2.4	2.7	2.9	3.1	3.3	3.6	3.8	4.0
2.8	1.6	1.9	2.1	2.4	2.6	2.9	3.1	3.3	3.6	3.8	4.1	4.3
3.0	1.8	2.0	2.3	2.5	2.8	3.1	3.3	3.6	3.8	4.1	4.4	4.6
3.2	1.9	2.2	2.4	2.7	3.0	3.3	3.5	3.8	4.1	4.4	4.7	4.9
3.4	2.0	2.3	2.6	2.9	3.2	3.5	3.8	4.1	4.4	4.7	5.0	5.3
3.6	2.1	2.4	2.7	3.1	3.4	3.7	4.0	4.3	4.6	4.9	5.2	5.6
3.8	2.2	2.6	2.9	3.2	3.6	3.9	4.2	4.5	4.9	5.2	5.5	5.9
4.0	2.3	2.7	3.0	3.4	3.7	4.1	4.4	4.8	5.1	5.5	5.8	6.2
4.2	2.5	2.8	3.2	3.6	3.9	4.3	4.7	5.0	5.4	5.8	6.1	6.5
4.4	2.6	3.0	3.3	3.7	4.1	4.5	4.9	5.3	5.6	6.0	6.4	6.8
4.6	2.7	3.1	3.5	3.9	4.3	4.7	5.1	5.5	5.9	6.3	6.7	7.1
4.8	2.8	3.2	3.6	4.1	4.5	4.9	5.3	5.7	6.2	6.6	7.0	7.4
5.0	2.9	3.4	3.8	4.2	4.7	5.1	5.5	6.0	6.4	6.9	7.3	7.7
5.2	3.0	3.5	4.0	4.4	4.9	5.3	5.8	6.2	6.7	7.1	7.6	8.0
5.4	3.2	3.6	4.1	4.6	5.0	5.5	6.0	6.5	6.9	7.4	7.9	8.3
5.6	3.3	3.8	4.3	4.7	5.2	5.7	6.2	6.7	7.2	7.7	8.2	8.6
5.8	3.4	3.9	4.4	4.9	5.4	5.9	6.4	6.9	7.4	7.9	8.5	9.0
6.0	3.5	4.0	4.6	5.1	5.6	6.1	6.7	7.2	7.7	8.2	8.7	9.3
6.2	3.6	4.2	4.7	5.3	5.8	6.3	6.9	7.4	8.0	8.5	9.0	9.6
6.4	3.8	4.3	4.9	5.4	6.0	6.5	7.1	7.7	8.2	8.8	9.3	9.9
6.6	3.9	4.4	5.0	5.6	6.2	6.7	7.3	7.9	8.5	9.0	9.6	10.2
6.8	4.0	4.6	5.2	5.8	6.4	6.9	7.5	8.1	8.7	9.3	9.9	10.5
7.0	4.1	4.7	5.3	5.9	6.6	7.2	7.8	8.4	9.0	9.6	10.2	10.8

Tidal Heights, ports

Heights in Metres

Pencil-mark height of H.W. Cherbourg - read from column below mark

Port	4.8	5.0	5.2	5.4	5.6	5.8	6.0	6.2	6.4	6.6	6.8	
PORTS, ENGLAND												
Lyme Regis	2.8	2.7	2.5	2.4	2.3	2.1	2.0	1.8	1.7	1.7	1.6	1.6
Bridport	2.7	2.6	2.4	2.3	2.2	2.0	1.9	1.7	1.6	1.6	1.5	1.5
Portland & Weymouth	1.0	0.9	0.9	0.8	0.7	0.6	0.5	0.4	0.3	0.3	0.2	0.2
Lulworth Cove	1.3	1.2	1.0	0.9	0.8	0.7	0.6	0.5	0.4	0.4	0.3	0.3
Swanage	1.2	1.1	1.1	1.0	0.9	0.8	0.7	0.5	0.4	0.3	0.2	0.1
Poole entrance	1.2	1.1	1.1	1.0	1.0	0.9	0.8	0.6	0.5	0.4	0.2	0.1
Poole Town Quay	1.5	1.4	1.4	1.3	1.3	1.2	1.1	0.9	0.8	0.7	0.7	0.6
Christchurch appr'ch	0.7	0.7	0.7	0.7	0.7	0.7	0.6	0.5	0.4	0.3	0.3	0.2
Christchurch Hbr	0.7	0.7	0.7	0.7	0.7	0.7	0.7	0.6	0.6	0.6	0.6	0.6
Lymington	1.7	1.6	1.6	1.5	1.5	1.4	1.3	1.3	1.2	1.1	1.1	1.0
Yarmouth I.o.W.	1.7	1.6	1.6	1.5	1.4	1.3	1.2	1.2	1.1	1.0	0.9	0.8
Cowes I.o.W.	2.3	2.2	2.2	2.1	2.1	2.0	1.9	1.9	1.8	1.7	1.6	1.5
Sandown I.o.W.	2.0	1.9	1.9	1.8	1.7	1.6	1.5	1.3	1.2	1.1	1.0	0.9
Southampton	1.9	2.0	2.0	2.1	2.2	2.2	2.3	2.3	2.4	2.4	2.3	2.3
Portsmouth	2.2	2.2	2.2	2.2	2.2	2.2	2.2	2.2	2.2	2.2	2.1	2.1
Chichester entrance	2.4	2.4	2.4	2.4	2.5	2.5	2.5	2.6	2.6	2.6	2.6	2.6
Selsey Bill	2.7	2.7	2.7	2.7	2.7	2.7	2.8	2.8	2.8	2.8	2.8	2.8
Littlehampton Hbr	2.2	2.3	2.5	2.6	2.7	2.8	3.0	3.1	3.2	3.2	3.3	3.3
Littlehampton appr'ch	2.7	2.7	2.7	2.7	2.8	2.8	2.8	2.9	2.9	2.9	3.0	3.0
Shoreham	2.7	2.6	2.6	2.5	2.4	2.4	2.3	2.3	2.2	2.2	2.1	2.1
Brighton	2.6	2.5	2.5	2.4	2.3	2.2	2.2	2.2	2.1	2.0	2.0	1.9
Newhaven	2.7	2.6	2.6	2.4	2.3	2.4	2.3	2.2	2.1	2.1	2.0	2.0
PORTS, FRANCE												
Le Havre	3.3	3.2	3.0	2.9	2.7	2.6	2.4	2.3	2.1	1.9	1.8	1.6
Honfleur	3.3	3.2	3.0	2.9	2.8	2.7	2.5	2.4	2.3	2.2	2.0	1.9
Trouville (Deauville)	3.3	3.1	2.9	2.7	2.5	2.4	2.2	2.0	1.8	1.6	1.5	1.3
Ouistreham	3.1	2.9	2.7	2.5	2.3	2.2	2.0	1.8	1.6	1.4	1.2	1.0
Courseulles	2.7	2.5	2.3	2.1	2.0	1.8	1.6	1.5	1.3	1.1	1.0	0.8
Arromanches	3.2	3.0	2.8	2.6	2.4	2.3	2.1	1.9	1.7	1.5	1.3	1.1
Port-en-Bessin	3.0	2.8	2.6	2.4	2.2	1.9	1.7	1.5	1.3	1.1	1.0	0.8
Saint-Vaast-la-Hougue	2.6	2.4	2.2	2.0	1.8	1.7	1.5	1.3	1.1	0.9	0.6	0.4
Barfleur	2.7	2.5	2.3	2.1	1.9	1.6	1.4	1.2	1.0	0.8	0.5	0.3
Cherbourg	2.9	2.7	2.5	2.3	2.1	1.9	1.7	1.5	1.3	1.0	0.8	0.5
Omonville	3.1	2.9	2.7	2.5	2.3	2.1	1.9	1.7	1.5	1.2	1.0	0.7
Goury	4.6	4.3	4.1	3.8	3.6	3.3	3.1	2.8	2.6	2.4	2.1	1.9
Dielette	5.3	5.0	4.8	4.5	4.2	4.0	3.7	3.5	3.2	3.0	2.8	2.6
Carteret	5.9	5.7	5.5	5.3	5.1	4.8	4.6	4.4	4.2	4.1	3.9	3.8
Granville	7.4	7.1	6.9	6.6	6.3	6.0	5.8	5.5	5.2	5.1	5.0	4.9
Saint Malo	7.1	6.8	6.6	6.3	6.0	5.7	5.4	5.1	4.8	4.6	4.5	4.3
All Hbrs, St Brieuc Bay	6.4	6.3	6.3	6.2	6.1	6.1	6.0	6.0	5.9	5.8	5.8	5.7
Paimpol	6.0	5.9	5.7	5.6	5.5	5.4	5.2	5.1	5.0	5.0	4.9	4.9
Ile de Bréhat	6.7	6.4	6.2	5.9	5.7	5.4	5.2	4.9	4.7	4.6	4.6	4.5
Lezardrieux	6.0	5.9	5.9	5.8	5.8	5.7	5.7	5.6	5.6	5.6	5.6	5.6
ISLANDS OFF												
Braye, Alderney	3.0	2.9	2.7	2.6	2.5	2.3	2.2	2.0	1.9	1.8	1.7	1.6
St Peter Port & Sark	5.1	4.9	4.7	4.5	4.3	4.2	4.0	3.8	3.6	3.3	3.2	3.1
St Helier, Jersey	6.2	5.9	5.7	5.4	5.2	4.9	4.7	4.4	4.2	4.1	3.9	3.8
St Catherine, Jersey	6.0	5.7	5.5	5.2	4.9	4.6	4.4	4.1	3.8	3.6	3.5	3.3
Les Minquiers	5.7	5.6	5.4	5.3	5.2	5.0	4.9	4.7	4.6	4.5	4.4	4.3
Iles Chausey	7.3	7.0	6.8	6.5	6.2	5.9	5.6	5.3	5.0	4.9	4.7	4.6

Coefficient de la marée

30 40 50 60 70 80 90 100 110

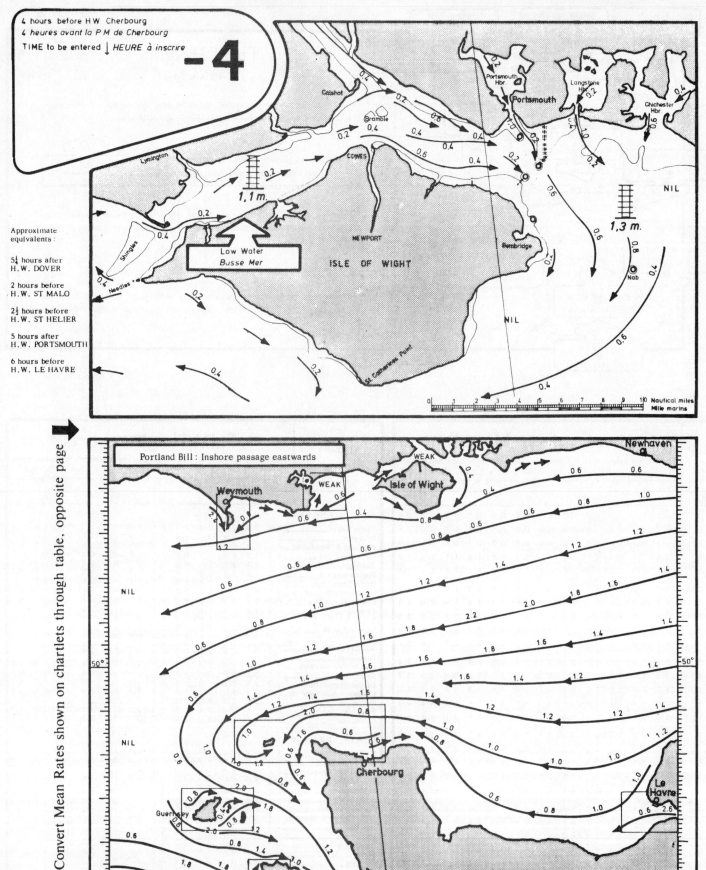

Approximate
equivalents :

5¼ hours after
H.W. DOVER

2 hours before
H.W. ST MALO

2½ hours before
H.W. ST HELIER

5 hours after
H.W. PORTSMOUTH

6 hours before
H.W. LE HAVRE

Low Water
Busse Mer

1,1 m.

1,3 m.

NIL

NIL

NIL

ISLE OF WIGHT

Lymington
Calshot
Bramble
COWES
NEWPORT
Bembridge
St Catherine's Point
Shingles
Needles
Portsmouth Hbr.
Portsmouth
Langstone Hbr.
Chichester Hbr.
Nab

0 1 2 3 4 5 6 7 8 9 10 Nautical miles
Mille marins

Convert Mean Rates shown on chartlets through table, opposite page

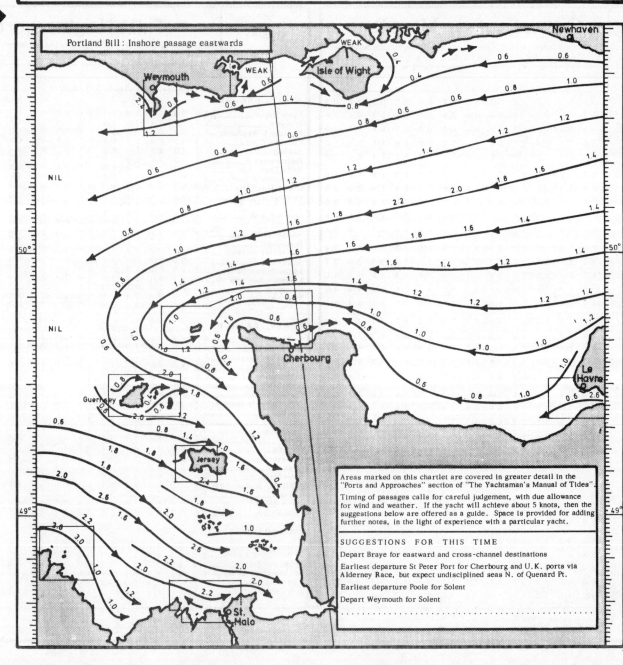

Portland Bill : Inshore passage eastwards

Weymouth
WEAK
WEAK
WEAK
Isle of Wight
Newhaven
NIL
NIL
50°
50°
Cherbourg
Guernsey
Jersey
Le Havre
49°
49°
St. Malo

Areas marked on this chartlet are covered in greater detail in the
"Ports and Approaches" section of "The Yachtsman's Manual of Tides".

Timing of passages calls for careful judgement, with due allowance
for wind and weather. If the yacht will achieve about 5 knots, then the
suggestions below are offered as a guide. Space is provided for adding
further notes, in the light of experience with a particular yacht.

SUGGESTIONS FOR THIS TIME

Depart Braye for eastward and cross-channel destinations

Earliest departure St Peter Port for Cherbourg and U.K. ports via
Alderney Race, but expect undisciplined seas N. of Quenard Pt.

Earliest departure Poole for Solent

Depart Weymouth for Solent

. . . .

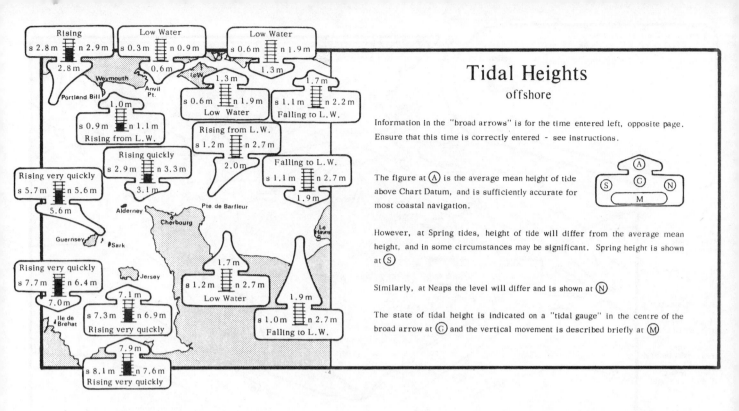

Tidal Heights
offshore

Information in the "broad arrows" is for the time entered left, opposite page. Ensure that this time is correctly entered - see instructions.

The figure at (A) is the average mean height of tide above Chart Datum, and is sufficiently accurate for most coastal navigation.

However, at Spring tides, height of tide will differ from the average mean height, and in some circumstances may be significant. Spring height is shown at (S)

Similarly, at Neaps the level will differ and is shown at (N)

The state of tidal height is indicated on a "tidal gauge" in the centre of the broad arrow at (G) and the vertical movement is described briefly at (M)

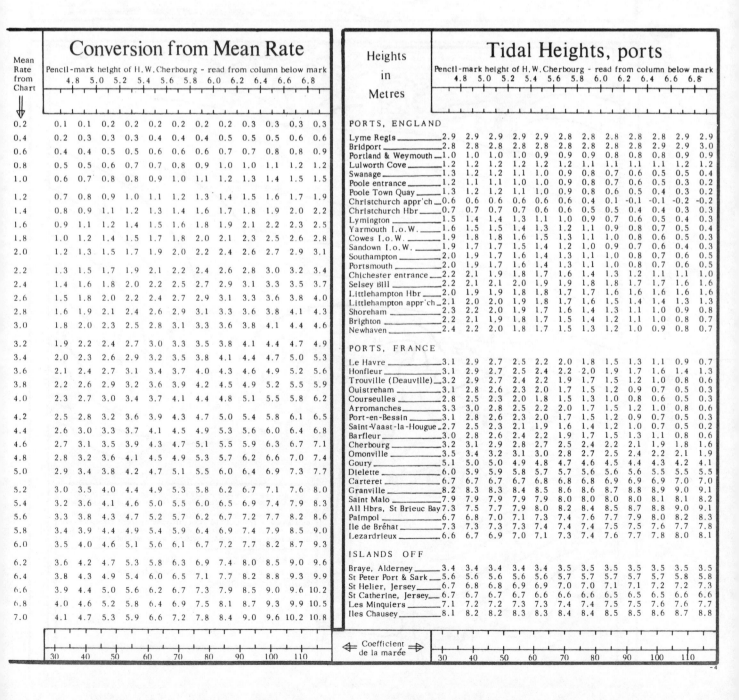

Conversion from Mean Rate

Pencil-mark height of H.W. Cherbourg - read from column below mark

Mean Rate from Chart	4.8	5.0	5.2	5.4	5.6	5.8	6.0	6.2	6.4	6.6	6.8	
0.2	0.1	0.1	0.2	0.2	0.2	0.2	0.2	0.2	0.3	0.3	0.3	0.3
0.4	0.2	0.3	0.3	0.3	0.4	0.4	0.4	0.5	0.5	0.5	0.6	0.6
0.6	0.4	0.4	0.5	0.5	0.6	0.6	0.6	0.7	0.7	0.8	0.8	0.9
0.8	0.5	0.5	0.6	0.7	0.7	0.8	0.9	1.0	1.0	1.1	1.2	1.2
1.0	0.6	0.7	0.8	0.8	0.9	1.0	1.1	1.2	1.3	1.4	1.5	1.5
1.2	0.7	0.8	0.9	1.0	1.1	1.2	1.3	1.4	1.5	1.6	1.7	1.9
1.4	0.8	0.9	1.1	1.2	1.3	1.4	1.6	1.7	1.8	1.9	2.0	2.2
1.6	0.9	1.1	1.2	1.4	1.5	1.6	1.8	1.9	2.1	2.2	2.3	2.5
1.8	1.0	1.2	1.4	1.5	1.7	1.8	2.0	2.1	2.3	2.5	2.6	2.8
2.0	1.2	1.3	1.5	1.7	1.9	2.0	2.2	2.4	2.6	2.7	2.9	3.1
2.2	1.3	1.5	1.7	1.9	2.1	2.2	2.4	2.6	2.8	3.0	3.2	3.4
2.4	1.4	1.6	1.8	2.0	2.2	2.5	2.7	2.9	3.1	3.3	3.5	3.7
2.6	1.5	1.8	2.0	2.2	2.4	2.7	2.9	3.1	3.3	3.6	3.8	4.0
2.8	1.6	1.9	2.1	2.4	2.6	2.9	3.1	3.3	3.6	3.8	4.1	4.3
3.0	1.8	2.0	2.3	2.5	2.8	3.1	3.3	3.6	3.8	4.1	4.4	4.6
3.2	1.9	2.2	2.4	2.7	3.0	3.3	3.5	3.8	4.1	4.4	4.7	4.9
3.4	2.0	2.3	2.6	2.9	3.2	3.5	3.8	4.1	4.4	4.7	5.0	5.3
3.6	2.1	2.4	2.7	3.1	3.4	3.7	4.0	4.3	4.6	4.9	5.2	5.6
3.8	2.2	2.6	2.9	3.2	3.6	3.9	4.2	4.5	4.9	5.2	5.5	5.9
4.0	2.3	2.7	3.0	3.4	3.7	4.1	4.4	4.8	5.1	5.5	5.8	6.2
4.2	2.5	2.8	3.2	3.6	3.9	4.3	4.7	5.0	5.4	5.8	6.1	6.5
4.4	2.6	3.0	3.3	3.7	4.1	4.5	4.9	5.3	5.6	6.0	6.4	6.8
4.6	2.7	3.1	3.5	3.9	4.3	4.7	5.1	5.5	5.9	6.3	6.7	7.1
4.8	2.8	3.2	3.6	4.1	4.5	4.9	5.3	5.7	6.2	6.6	7.0	7.4
5.0	2.9	3.4	3.8	4.2	4.7	5.1	5.5	6.0	6.4	6.9	7.3	7.7
5.2	3.0	3.5	4.0	4.4	4.9	5.3	5.8	6.2	6.7	7.1	7.6	8.0
5.4	3.2	3.6	4.1	4.6	5.0	5.5	6.0	6.5	6.9	7.4	7.9	8.3
5.6	3.3	3.8	4.3	4.7	5.2	5.7	6.2	6.7	7.2	7.7	8.2	8.6
5.8	3.4	3.9	4.4	4.9	5.4	5.9	6.4	6.9	7.4	7.9	8.5	9.0
6.0	3.5	4.0	4.6	5.1	5.6	6.1	6.7	7.2	7.7	8.2	8.7	9.3
6.2	3.6	4.2	4.7	5.3	5.8	6.3	6.9	7.4	8.0	8.5	9.0	9.6
6.4	3.8	4.3	4.9	5.4	6.0	6.5	7.1	7.7	8.2	8.8	9.3	9.9
6.6	3.9	4.4	5.0	5.6	6.2	6.7	7.3	7.9	8.5	9.0	9.6	10.2
6.8	4.0	4.6	5.2	5.8	6.4	6.9	7.5	8.1	8.7	9.3	9.9	10.5
7.0	4.1	4.7	5.3	5.9	6.6	7.2	7.8	8.4	9.0	9.6	10.2	10.8

Tidal Heights, ports

Heights in Metres

Pencil-mark height of H.W. Cherbourg - read from column below mark

	4.8	5.0	5.2	5.4	5.6	5.8	6.0	6.2	6.4	6.6	6.8	
PORTS, ENGLAND												
Lyme Regis	2.9	2.9	2.9	2.9	2.9	2.8	2.8	2.8	2.8	2.8	2.9	2.9
Bridport	2.8	2.8	2.8	2.8	2.8	2.8	2.8	2.8	2.8	2.9	2.9	3.0
Portland & Weymouth	1.0	1.0	1.0	1.0	0.9	0.9	0.9	0.8	0.8	0.8	0.9	0.9
Lulworth Cove	1.2	1.2	1.2	1.2	1.2	1.2	1.1	1.1	1.1	1.1	1.2	1.2
Swanage	1.3	1.2	1.2	1.1	1.0	0.9	0.8	0.7	0.6	0.5	0.5	0.4
Poole entrance	1.2	1.1	1.1	1.0	1.0	0.9	0.8	0.7	0.6	0.5	0.3	0.2
Poole Town Quay	1.3	1.2	1.2	1.1	1.0	0.9	0.8	0.6	0.5	0.4	0.3	0.2
Christchurch appr'ch	0.6	0.6	0.6	0.6	0.6	0.6	0.4	0.1	-0.1	-0.1	-0.2	-0.2
Christchurch Hbr	0.7	0.7	0.7	0.7	0.6	0.6	0.5	0.5	0.4	0.4	0.3	0.3
Lymington	1.5	1.4	1.4	1.3	1.1	1.0	0.9	0.7	0.6	0.5	0.4	0.3
Yarmouth I.o.W.	1.6	1.5	1.5	1.4	1.3	1.2	1.1	0.9	0.8	0.7	0.5	0.4
Cowes I.o.W.	1.9	1.8	1.8	1.6	1.5	1.3	1.1	1.0	0.8	0.6	0.5	0.3
Sandown I.o.W.	1.9	1.7	1.7	1.5	1.4	1.2	1.0	0.9	0.7	0.6	0.4	0.3
Southampton	2.0	1.9	1.7	1.6	1.4	1.3	1.1	1.0	0.8	0.7	0.6	0.5
Portsmouth	2.0	1.9	1.7	1.6	1.4	1.3	1.1	1.0	0.8	0.7	0.6	0.5
Chichester entrance	2.2	2.1	1.9	1.8	1.7	1.6	1.4	1.3	1.2	1.1	1.1	1.0
Selsey Bill	2.2	2.1	2.1	2.0	1.9	1.9	1.8	1.8	1.7	1.7	1.6	1.6
Littlehampton Hbr	2.0	1.9	1.9	1.8	1.8	1.7	1.7	1.6	1.6	1.6	1.6	1.6
Littlehampton appr'ch	2.1	2.0	2.0	1.9	1.8	1.7	1.6	1.5	1.4	1.4	1.3	1.3
Shoreham	2.3	2.2	2.0	1.9	1.7	1.6	1.4	1.3	1.1	1.0	0.9	0.8
Brighton	2.2	2.1	1.9	1.8	1.7	1.5	1.4	1.2	1.1	1.0	0.8	0.7
Newhaven	2.4	2.2	2.0	1.8	1.7	1.5	1.3	1.2	1.0	0.9	0.8	0.7
PORTS, FRANCE												
Le Havre	3.1	2.9	2.7	2.5	2.2	2.0	1.8	1.5	1.3	1.1	0.9	0.7
Honfleur	3.1	2.9	2.7	2.5	2.4	2.2	2.0	1.9	1.7	1.6	1.4	1.3
Trouville (Deauville)	3.2	2.9	2.7	2.4	2.2	1.9	1.7	1.5	1.2	1.0	0.8	0.6
Ouistreham	3.1	2.8	2.6	2.3	2.0	1.7	1.5	1.2	0.9	0.7	0.5	0.3
Courseulles	2.8	2.5	2.3	2.0	1.8	1.5	1.3	1.0	0.8	0.6	0.5	0.3
Arromanches	3.3	3.0	2.8	2.5	2.2	2.0	1.7	1.5	1.2	1.0	0.8	0.6
Port-en-Bessin	3.1	2.8	2.6	2.3	2.0	1.7	1.5	1.2	0.9	0.7	0.5	0.3
Saint-Vaast-la-Hougue	2.7	2.5	2.3	2.1	1.9	1.6	1.4	1.2	1.0	0.7	0.5	0.2
Barfleur	3.0	2.8	2.6	2.4	2.2	1.9	1.7	1.5	1.3	1.1	0.8	0.6
Cherbourg	3.2	3.1	2.9	2.8	2.7	2.5	2.4	2.2	2.1	1.9	1.8	1.6
Omonville	3.5	3.4	3.2	3.1	3.0	2.8	2.7	2.5	2.4	2.2	2.1	1.9
Goury	5.1	5.0	5.0	4.9	4.8	4.7	4.6	4.5	4.4	4.3	4.2	4.1
Diélette	6.0	5.9	5.9	5.8	5.7	5.7	5.6	5.6	5.6	5.5	5.5	5.5
Carteret	6.7	6.7	6.7	6.7	6.8	6.8	6.8	6.9	6.9	6.9	7.0	7.0
Granville	8.2	8.3	8.3	8.4	8.5	8.6	8.6	8.7	8.8	8.9	9.0	9.1
Saint Malo	7.9	7.9	7.9	7.9	7.9	8.0	8.0	8.0	8.0	8.1	8.1	8.2
All Hbrs, St Brieuc Bay	7.3	7.5	7.7	7.9	8.0	8.2	8.4	8.5	8.7	8.8	9.0	9.1
Paimpol	6.7	6.8	7.0	7.1	7.3	7.4	7.6	7.7	7.9	8.0	8.2	8.3
Ile de Bréhat	7.3	7.3	7.3	7.3	7.4	7.4	7.4	7.5	7.5	7.6	7.7	7.8
Lézardrieux	6.6	6.7	6.9	7.0	7.1	7.3	7.4	7.6	7.7	7.8	8.0	8.1
ISLANDS OFF												
Braye, Alderney	3.4	3.4	3.4	3.4	3.4	3.5	3.5	3.5	3.5	3.5	3.5	3.5
St Peter Port & Sark	5.6	5.6	5.6	5.6	5.6	5.7	5.7	5.7	5.7	5.7	5.8	5.8
St Helier, Jersey	6.7	6.6	6.8	6.9	6.9	7.0	7.0	7.1	7.1	7.2	7.2	7.3
St Catherine, Jersey	6.7	6.7	6.7	6.7	6.6	6.6	6.6	6.5	6.5	6.5	6.6	6.6
Les Minquiers	7.1	7.2	7.2	7.3	7.3	7.4	7.4	7.5	7.5	7.6	7.6	7.7
Iles Chausey	8.1	8.2	8.2	8.3	8.3	8.4	8.4	8.5	8.5	8.6	8.7	8.8

Coefficient de la marée

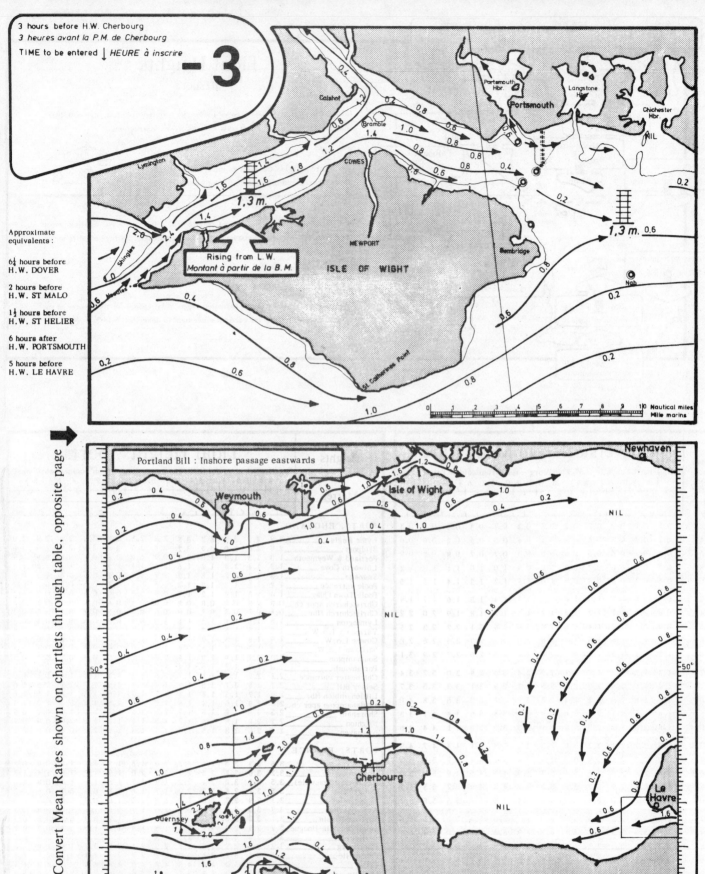

-3

Approximate
equivalents :

6¼ hours before
H.W. DOVER

2 hours before
H.W. ST MALO

1½ hours before
H.W. ST HELIER

6 hours after
H.W. PORTSMOUTH

5 hours before
H.W. LE HAVRE

1,3 m.

Rising from L.W.
Montant à partir de la B.M.

ISLE OF WIGHT

Portsmouth

Langstone Hbr.

Chichester Hbr.

NIL

Calshot

Bramble

COWES

NEWPORT

Bembridge

Nab

Lymington

Shingles

Needles

St. Catherine's Point

0 1 2 3 4 5 6 7 8 9 10 Nautical miles
Mile marins

Convert Mean Rates shown on chartlets through table, opposite page

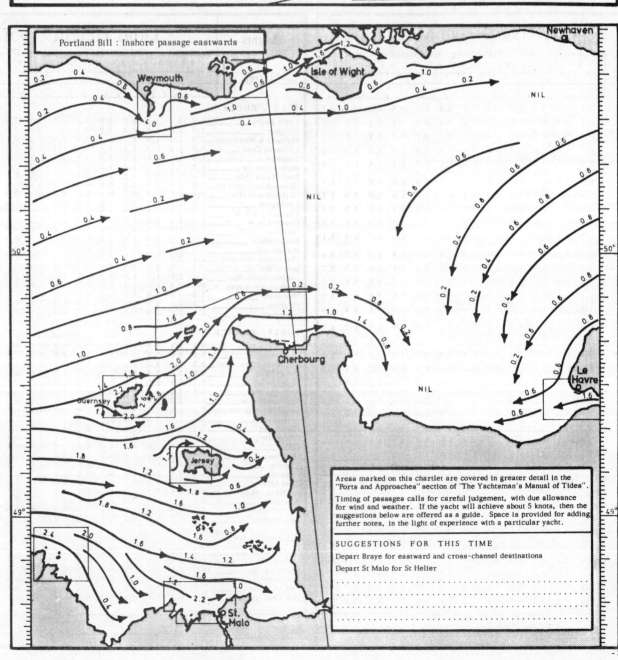

Portland Bill : Inshore passage eastwards

Newhaven

Weymouth

Isle of Wight

NIL

NIL

NIL

Cherbourg

Guernsey

Le Havre

Jersey

St. Malo

50°

49°

Areas marked on this chartlet are covered in greater detail in the
"Ports and Approaches" section of "The Yachtsman's Manual of Tides".

Timing of passages calls for careful judgement, with due allowance
for wind and weather. If the yacht will achieve about 5 knots, then the
suggestions below are offered as a guide. Space is provided for adding
further notes, in the light of experience with a particular yacht.

SUGGESTIONS FOR THIS TIME

Depart Braye for eastward and cross-channel destinations
Depart St Malo for St Helier

. . . .
. . . .
. . . .
. . . .

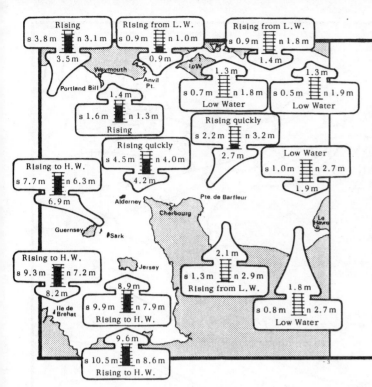

Tidal Heights
offshore

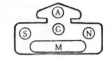

Information in the "broad arrows" is for the time entered left, opposite page. Ensure that this time is correctly entered - see instructions.

The figure at (A) is the average mean height of tide above Chart Datum, and is sufficiently accurate for most coastal navigation.

However, at Spring tides, height of tide will differ from the average mean height, and in some circumstances may be significant. Spring height is shown at (S)

Similarly, at Neaps the level will differ and is shown at (N)

The state of tidal height is indicated on a "tidal gauge" in the centre of the broad arrow at (G) and the vertical movement is described briefly at (M)

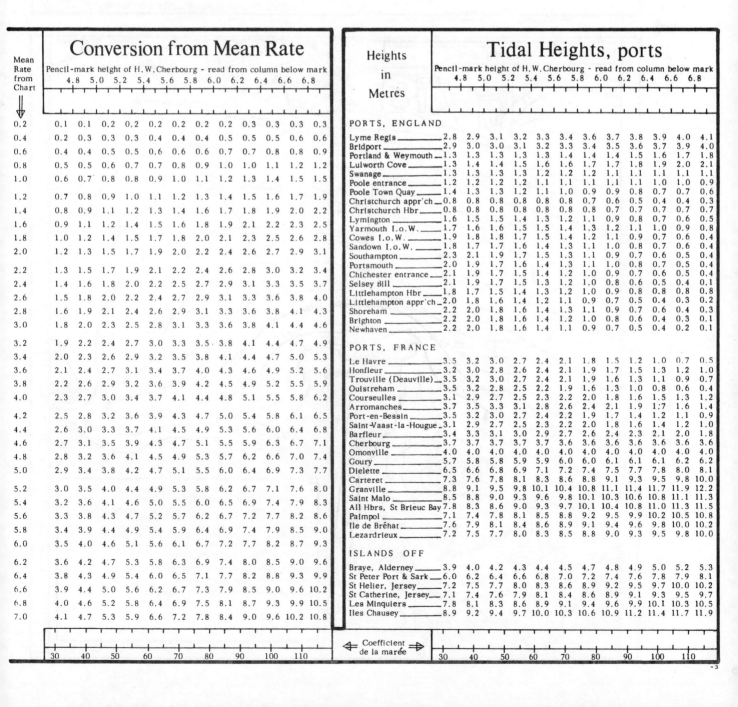

Conversion from Mean Rate

Pencil-mark height of H.W. Cherbourg - read from column below mark

Mean Rate from Chart	4.8	5.0	5.2	5.4	5.6	5.8	6.0	6.2	6.4	6.6	6.8	
0.2	0.1	0.1	0.2	0.2	0.2	0.2	0.2	0.2	0.3	0.3	0.3	0.3
0.4	0.2	0.3	0.3	0.3	0.4	0.4	0.4	0.5	0.5	0.5	0.6	0.6
0.6	0.4	0.4	0.5	0.5	0.6	0.6	0.6	0.7	0.7	0.8	0.8	0.9
0.8	0.5	0.5	0.6	0.7	0.7	0.8	0.9	1.0	1.0	1.1	1.2	1.2
1.0	0.6	0.7	0.8	0.8	0.9	1.0	1.1	1.2	1.3	1.4	1.5	1.5
1.2	0.7	0.8	0.9	1.0	1.1	1.2	1.3	1.4	1.5	1.6	1.7	1.9
1.4	0.8	0.9	1.1	1.2	1.3	1.4	1.6	1.7	1.8	1.9	2.0	2.2
1.6	0.9	1.1	1.2	1.4	1.5	1.6	1.8	1.9	2.1	2.2	2.3	2.5
1.8	1.0	1.2	1.4	1.5	1.7	1.8	2.0	2.1	2.3	2.5	2.6	2.8
2.0	1.2	1.3	1.5	1.7	1.9	2.0	2.2	2.4	2.6	2.7	2.9	3.1
2.2	1.3	1.5	1.7	1.9	2.1	2.2	2.4	2.6	2.8	3.0	3.2	3.4
2.4	1.4	1.6	1.8	2.0	2.2	2.5	2.7	2.9	3.1	3.3	3.5	3.7
2.6	1.5	1.8	2.0	2.2	2.4	2.7	2.9	3.1	3.3	3.6	3.8	4.0
2.8	1.6	1.9	2.1	2.4	2.6	2.9	3.1	3.3	3.6	3.8	4.1	4.3
3.0	1.8	2.0	2.3	2.5	2.8	3.1	3.3	3.6	3.8	4.1	4.4	4.6
3.2	1.9	2.2	2.4	2.7	3.0	3.3	3.5	3.8	4.1	4.4	4.7	4.9
3.4	2.0	2.3	2.6	2.9	3.2	3.5	3.8	4.1	4.4	4.7	5.0	5.3
3.6	2.1	2.4	2.7	3.1	3.4	3.7	4.0	4.3	4.6	4.9	5.2	5.6
3.8	2.2	2.6	2.9	3.2	3.6	3.9	4.2	4.5	4.9	5.2	5.5	5.9
4.0	2.3	2.7	3.0	3.4	3.7	4.1	4.4	4.8	5.1	5.5	5.8	6.2
4.2	2.5	2.8	3.2	3.6	3.9	4.3	4.7	5.0	5.4	5.8	6.1	6.5
4.4	2.6	3.0	3.3	3.7	4.1	4.5	4.9	5.3	5.6	6.0	6.4	6.8
4.6	2.7	3.1	3.5	3.9	4.3	4.7	5.1	5.5	5.9	6.3	6.7	7.1
4.8	2.8	3.2	3.6	4.1	4.5	4.9	5.3	5.7	6.2	6.6	7.0	7.4
5.0	2.9	3.4	3.8	4.2	4.7	5.1	5.5	6.0	6.4	6.9	7.3	7.7
5.2	3.0	3.5	4.0	4.4	4.9	5.3	5.8	6.2	6.7	7.1	7.6	8.0
5.4	3.2	3.6	4.1	4.6	5.0	5.5	6.0	6.5	6.9	7.4	7.9	8.3
5.6	3.3	3.8	4.3	4.8	5.2	5.7	6.2	6.7	7.2	7.7	8.2	8.6
5.8	3.4	3.9	4.4	4.9	5.4	5.9	6.4	6.9	7.4	7.9	8.5	9.0
6.0	3.5	4.0	4.6	5.1	5.6	6.1	6.7	7.2	7.7	8.2	8.7	9.3
6.2	3.6	4.2	4.7	5.3	5.8	6.3	6.9	7.4	8.0	8.5	9.0	9.6
6.4	3.8	4.3	4.9	5.4	6.0	6.5	7.1	7.7	8.2	8.8	9.3	9.9
6.6	3.9	4.4	5.0	5.6	6.2	6.7	7.3	7.9	8.5	9.0	9.6	10.2
6.8	4.0	4.6	5.2	5.8	6.4	6.9	7.5	8.1	8.7	9.3	9.9	10.5
7.0	4.1	4.7	5.3	5.9	6.6	7.2	7.8	8.4	9.0	9.6	10.2	10.8

Tidal Heights, ports

Heights in Metres

Pencil-mark height of H.W. Cherbourg - read from column below mark

Heights in Metres	4.8	5.0	5.2	5.4	5.6	5.8	6.0	6.2	6.4	6.6	6.8	
PORTS, ENGLAND												
Lyme Regis	2.8	2.9	3.1	3.2	3.3	3.4	3.6	3.7	3.8	3.9	4.0	4.1
Bridport	2.9	3.0	3.0	3.1	3.2	3.3	3.4	3.5	3.6	3.7	3.9	4.0
Portland & Weymouth	1.3	1.3	1.3	1.3	1.3	1.4	1.4	1.4	1.5	1.6	1.7	1.8
Lulworth Cove	1.3	1.4	1.4	1.5	1.6	1.6	1.7	1.7	1.8	1.9	2.0	2.1
Swanage	1.3	1.3	1.3	1.3	1.2	1.2	1.2	1.1	1.1	1.1	1.1	1.1
Poole entrance	1.2	1.2	1.2	1.2	1.1	1.1	1.1	1.1	1.1	1.0	1.0	0.9
Poole Town Quay	1.4	1.3	1.3	1.2	1.1	1.0	0.9	0.9	0.8	0.7	0.7	0.6
Christchurch appr'ch	0.8	0.8	0.8	0.8	0.8	0.8	0.7	0.6	0.5	0.4	0.4	0.3
Christchurch Hbr	0.8	0.8	0.8	0.8	0.8	0.8	0.8	0.7	0.7	0.7	0.7	0.7
Lymington	1.6	1.5	1.5	1.4	1.3	1.2	1.1	0.9	0.8	0.7	0.6	0.5
Yarmouth I.o.W.	1.7	1.6	1.6	1.5	1.5	1.4	1.3	1.2	1.1	1.0	0.9	0.8
Cowes I.o.W.	1.9	1.8	1.8	1.7	1.5	1.4	1.2	1.1	0.9	0.7	0.6	0.4
Sandown I.o.W.	1.8	1.7	1.7	1.6	1.4	1.3	1.1	1.0	0.8	0.7	0.6	0.4
Southampton	2.3	2.1	1.9	1.7	1.5	1.3	1.1	0.9	0.7	0.6	0.5	0.4
Portsmouth	2.0	1.9	1.7	1.6	1.4	1.3	1.1	1.0	0.8	0.7	0.5	0.4
Chichester entrance	2.1	1.9	1.7	1.5	1.4	1.2	1.0	0.9	0.7	0.6	0.5	0.4
Selsey Bill	2.1	1.9	1.7	1.5	1.3	1.2	1.0	0.8	0.6	0.5	0.4	0.1
Littlehampton Hbr	1.8	1.7	1.5	1.4	1.3	1.2	1.0	0.9	0.8	0.8	0.8	0.8
Littlehampton appr'ch	2.0	1.8	1.6	1.4	1.2	1.1	0.9	0.7	0.5	0.4	0.3	0.2
Shoreham	2.2	2.0	1.8	1.6	1.4	1.3	1.1	0.9	0.7	0.6	0.4	0.3
Brighton	2.2	2.0	1.8	1.6	1.4	1.2	1.0	0.8	0.6	0.4	0.3	0.1
Newhaven	2.2	2.0	1.8	1.6	1.4	1.1	0.9	0.7	0.5	0.4	0.2	0.1
PORTS, FRANCE												
Le Havre	3.5	3.2	3.0	2.7	2.4	2.1	1.8	1.5	1.2	1.0	0.7	0.5
Honfleur	3.2	3.0	2.8	2.6	2.4	2.1	1.9	1.7	1.5	1.3	1.2	1.0
Trouville (Deauville)	3.5	3.2	3.0	2.7	2.4	2.1	1.9	1.6	1.3	1.1	0.9	0.7
Ouistreham	3.5	3.2	2.8	2.5	2.2	1.9	1.6	1.3	1.0	0.8	0.6	0.4
Courseulles	3.1	2.9	2.7	2.5	2.3	2.2	2.0	1.8	1.6	1.5	1.3	1.2
Arromanches	3.7	3.5	3.3	3.1	2.8	2.6	2.4	2.1	1.9	1.7	1.6	1.4
Port-en-Bessin	3.5	3.2	3.0	2.7	2.4	2.2	1.9	1.7	1.4	1.2	1.1	0.9
Saint-Vaast-la-Hougue	3.1	2.9	2.7	2.5	2.3	2.2	2.0	1.8	1.6	1.4	1.2	1.0
Barfleur	3.4	3.3	3.1	3.0	2.9	2.7	2.6	2.4	2.3	2.1	2.0	1.8
Cherbourg	3.7	3.7	3.7	3.7	3.7	3.6	3.6	3.6	3.6	3.6	3.6	3.6
Omonville	4.0	4.0	4.0	4.0	4.0	4.0	4.0	4.0	4.0	4.0	4.0	4.0
Goury	5.7	5.8	5.8	5.9	5.9	6.0	6.0	6.1	6.1	6.1	6.2	6.2
Dielette	6.5	6.6	6.8	6.9	7.1	7.2	7.4	7.5	7.7	7.8	8.0	8.1
Carteret	7.3	7.6	7.8	8.1	8.3	8.6	8.8	9.1	9.3	9.5	9.8	10.0
Granville	8.8	9.1	9.5	9.8	10.1	10.4	10.8	11.1	11.4	11.7	11.9	12.2
Saint Malo	8.5	8.8	9.0	9.3	9.6	9.8	10.1	10.3	10.6	10.8	11.1	11.3
All Hbrs, St Brieuc Bay	7.8	8.3	8.6	9.0	9.3	9.7	10.1	10.4	10.8	11.0	11.3	11.5
Paimpol	7.1	7.4	7.8	8.1	8.5	8.8	9.2	9.5	9.9	10.2	10.5	10.8
Ile de Bréhat	7.6	7.9	8.1	8.4	8.6	8.9	9.1	9.4	9.6	9.8	10.0	10.2
Lezardrieux	7.2	7.5	7.7	8.0	8.3	8.5	8.8	9.0	9.3	9.5	9.8	10.0
ISLANDS OFF												
Braye, Alderney	3.9	4.0	4.2	4.3	4.4	4.5	4.7	4.8	4.9	5.0	5.2	5.3
St Peter Port & Sark	6.0	6.2	6.4	6.6	6.8	7.0	7.2	7.4	7.6	7.8	7.9	8.1
St Helier, Jersey	7.2	7.5	7.7	8.0	8.3	8.6	8.9	9.2	9.5	9.7	10.0	10.2
St Catherine, Jersey	7.1	7.4	7.6	7.9	8.1	8.4	8.6	8.9	9.1	9.3	9.5	9.7
Les Minquiers	7.8	8.1	8.3	8.6	8.9	9.1	9.4	9.6	9.9	10.1	10.3	10.5
Iles Chausey	8.9	9.2	9.4	9.7	10.0	10.3	10.6	10.9	11.2	11.4	11.7	11.9

⇐ Coefficient de la marée ⇒

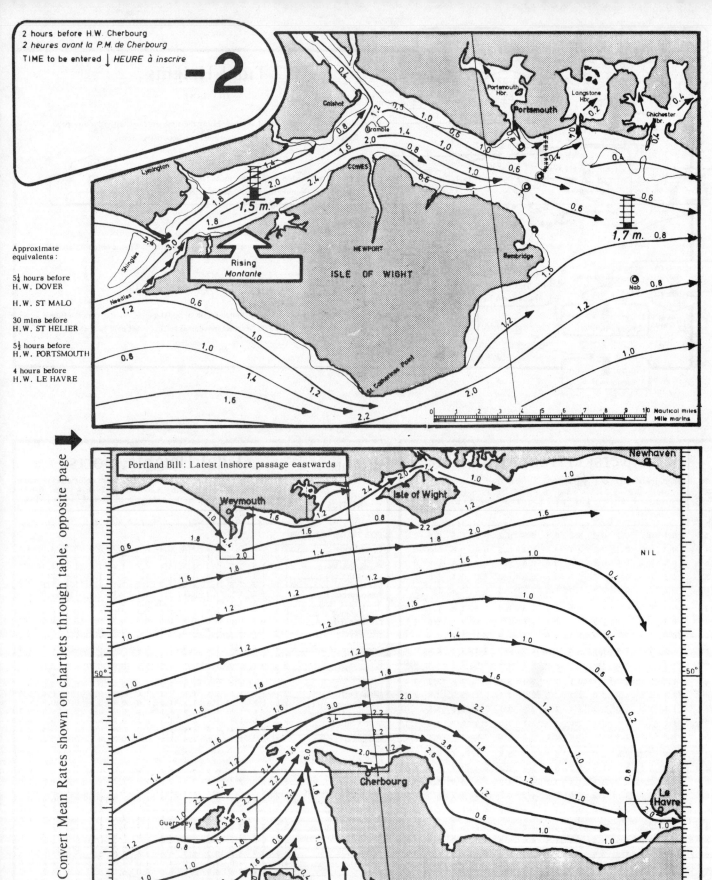

Approximate
equivalents :

5¼ hours before
H.W. DOVER

H.W. ST MALO

30 mins before
H.W. ST HELIER

5½ hours before
H.W. PORTSMOUTH

4 hours before
H.W. LE HAVRE

Rising
Montante

ISLE OF WIGHT

1,5 m.

1,7 m.

Nab

0 1 2 3 4 5 6 7 8 9 10 Nautical miles
Mille marins

Convert Mean Rates shown on chartlets through table, opposite page

Portland Bill : Latest inshore passage eastwards

Weymouth

Isle of Wight

Newhaven

NIL

Guernsey

Cherbourg

La Havre

Jersey

WEAK

WEAK

St. Malo

Areas marked on this chartlet are covered in greater detail in the
"Ports and Approaches" section of "The Yachtsman's Manual of Tides".

Timing of passages calls for careful judgement, with due allowance
for wind and weather. If the yacht will achieve about 5 knots, then the
suggestions below are offered as a guide. Space is provided for adding
further notes, in the light of experience with a particular yacht.

SUGGESTIONS FOR THIS TIME

Best departure St Helier for St Peter Port
Best departure St Malo for Lezardrieux
Suggested departure Granville for St Malo

. . . .
. . . .
. . . .

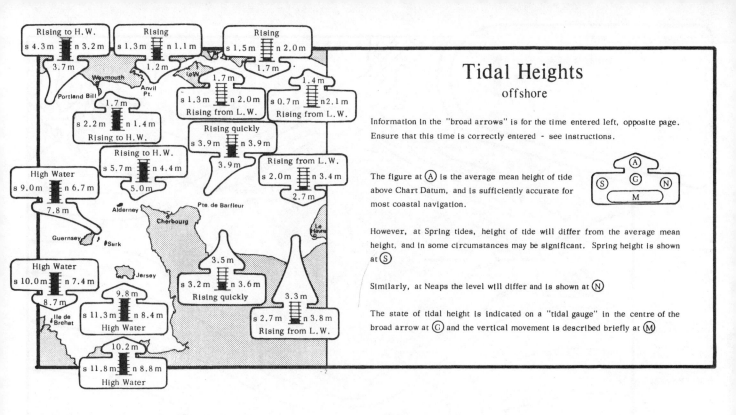

Tidal Heights
offshore

Information in the "broad arrows" is for the time entered left, opposite page. Ensure that this time is correctly entered - see instructions.

The figure at (A) is the average mean height of tide above Chart Datum, and is sufficiently accurate for most coastal navigation.

However, at Spring tides, height of tide will differ from the average mean height, and in some circumstances may be significant. Spring height is shown at (S)

Similarly, at Neaps the level will differ and is shown at (N)

The state of tidal height is indicated on a "tidal gauge" in the centre of the broad arrow at (G) and the vertical movement is described briefly at (M)

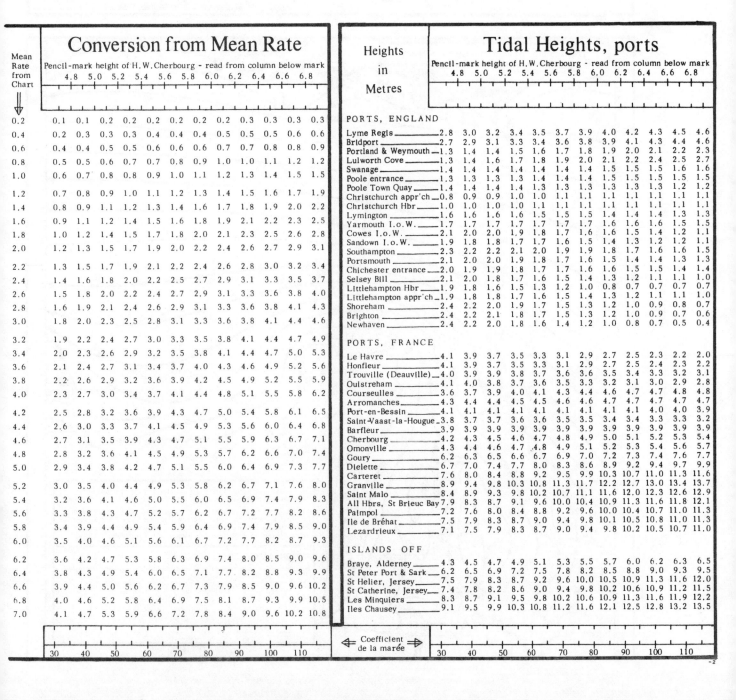

Conversion from Mean Rate

Pencil-mark height of H.W. Cherbourg - read from column below mark

Mean Rate from Chart ⇓	4.8	5.0	5.2	5.4	5.6	5.8	6.0	6.2	6.4	6.6	6.8
0.2	0.1	0.1	0.2	0.2	0.2	0.2	0.2	0.2	0.3	0.3	0.3
0.4	0.2	0.3	0.3	0.3	0.4	0.4	0.4	0.5	0.5	0.5	0.6
0.6	0.4	0.4	0.5	0.5	0.6	0.6	0.6	0.7	0.7	0.8	0.8
0.8	0.5	0.5	0.6	0.7	0.7	0.8	0.9	1.0	1.0	1.1	1.2
1.0	0.6	0.7	0.8	0.8	0.9	1.0	1.1	1.2	1.3	1.4	1.5
1.2	0.7	0.8	0.9	1.0	1.1	1.2	1.3	1.4	1.5	1.6	1.7
1.4	0.8	0.9	1.1	1.2	1.3	1.4	1.6	1.7	1.8	1.9	2.0
1.6	0.9	1.1	1.2	1.4	1.5	1.6	1.8	1.9	2.1	2.2	2.3
1.8	1.0	1.2	1.4	1.5	1.7	1.8	2.0	2.1	2.3	2.5	2.6
2.0	1.2	1.3	1.5	1.7	1.9	2.0	2.2	2.4	2.6	2.7	2.9
2.2	1.3	1.5	1.7	1.9	2.1	2.2	2.4	2.6	2.8	3.0	3.2
2.4	1.4	1.6	1.8	2.0	2.2	2.5	2.7	2.9	3.1	3.3	3.5
2.6	1.5	1.8	2.0	2.2	2.4	2.7	2.9	3.1	3.3	3.6	3.8
2.8	1.6	1.9	2.1	2.4	2.6	2.9	3.1	3.3	3.6	3.8	4.1
3.0	1.8	2.0	2.3	2.5	2.8	3.1	3.3	3.6	3.8	4.1	4.4
3.2	1.9	2.2	2.4	2.7	3.0	3.3	3.5	3.8	4.1	4.4	4.7
3.4	2.0	2.3	2.6	2.9	3.2	3.5	3.8	4.1	4.4	4.7	5.0
3.6	2.1	2.4	2.7	3.1	3.4	3.7	4.0	4.3	4.6	4.9	5.2
3.8	2.2	2.6	2.9	3.2	3.6	3.9	4.2	4.5	4.9	5.2	5.5
4.0	2.3	2.7	3.0	3.4	3.7	4.1	4.4	4.8	5.1	5.5	5.8
4.2	2.5	2.8	3.2	3.6	3.9	4.3	4.7	5.0	5.4	5.8	6.1
4.4	2.6	3.0	3.3	3.7	4.1	4.5	4.9	5.3	5.6	6.0	6.4
4.6	2.7	3.1	3.5	3.9	4.3	4.7	5.1	5.5	5.9	6.3	6.7
4.8	2.8	3.2	3.6	4.1	4.5	4.9	5.3	5.7	6.2	6.6	7.0
5.0	2.9	3.4	3.8	4.2	4.7	5.1	5.5	6.0	6.4	6.9	7.3
5.2	3.0	3.5	4.0	4.4	4.9	5.3	5.8	6.2	6.7	7.1	7.6
5.4	3.2	3.6	4.1	4.6	5.0	5.5	6.0	6.5	6.9	7.4	7.9
5.6	3.3	3.8	4.3	4.7	5.2	5.7	6.2	6.7	7.2	7.7	8.2
5.8	3.4	3.9	4.4	4.9	5.4	5.9	6.4	6.9	7.4	7.9	8.5
6.0	3.5	4.0	4.6	5.1	5.6	6.1	6.7	7.2	7.7	8.2	8.7
6.2	3.6	4.2	4.7	5.3	5.8	6.3	6.9	7.4	8.0	8.5	9.0
6.4	3.8	4.3	4.9	5.4	6.0	6.5	7.1	7.7	8.2	8.8	9.3
6.6	3.9	4.4	5.0	5.6	6.2	6.7	7.3	7.9	8.5	9.0	9.6
6.8	4.0	4.6	5.2	5.8	6.4	6.9	7.5	8.1	8.7	9.3	9.9
7.0	4.1	4.7	5.3	5.9	6.6	7.2	7.8	8.4	9.0	9.6	10.2

(The 6.8 column values, continuing each row: 0.2→0.3, 0.4→0.6, 0.6→0.9, 0.8→1.2, 1.0→1.5, 1.2→1.9, 1.4→2.2, 1.6→2.5, 1.8→2.8, 2.0→3.1, 2.2→3.4, 2.4→3.7, 2.6→4.0, 2.8→4.3, 3.0→4.6, 3.2→4.9, 3.4→5.3, 3.6→5.6, 3.8→5.9, 4.0→6.2, 4.2→6.5, 4.4→6.8, 4.6→7.1, 4.8→7.4, 5.0→7.7, 5.2→8.0, 5.4→8.3, 5.6→8.6, 5.8→9.0, 6.0→9.3, 6.2→9.6, 6.4→9.9, 6.6→10.2, 6.8→10.5, 7.0→10.8)

Tidal Heights, ports
Heights in Metres

Pencil-mark height of H.W. Cherbourg - read from column below mark

PORTS, ENGLAND

		4.8	5.0	5.2	5.4	5.6	5.8	6.0	6.2	6.4	6.6	6.8
Lyme Regis	2.8	3.0	3.2	3.4	3.5	3.7	3.9	4.0	4.2	4.3	4.5	4.6
Bridport	2.7	2.9	3.1	3.3	3.4	3.6	3.8	3.9	4.1	4.3	4.4	4.6
Portland & Weymouth	1.3	1.4	1.4	1.5	1.6	1.7	1.8	1.9	2.0	2.1	2.2	2.3
Lulworth Cove	1.3	1.4	1.6	1.7	1.8	1.9	2.0	2.1	2.2	2.4	2.5	2.7
Swanage	1.4	1.4	1.4	1.4	1.4	1.4	1.4	1.5	1.5	1.5	1.6	1.6
Poole entrance	1.3	1.3	1.3	1.3	1.4	1.4	1.4	1.5	1.5	1.5	1.5	1.5
Poole Town Quay	1.4	1.4	1.4	1.4	1.3	1.3	1.3	1.3	1.3	1.3	1.2	1.2
Christchurch appr'ch	0.8	0.9	0.9	1.0	1.0	1.1	1.1	1.1	1.1	1.1	1.1	1.1
Christchurch Hbr	1.0	1.0	1.0	1.0	1.1	1.1	1.1	1.1	1.1	1.1	1.1	1.1
Lymington	1.6	1.6	1.6	1.6	1.5	1.5	1.5	1.4	1.4	1.4	1.3	1.3
Yarmouth I.o.W.	1.7	1.7	1.7	1.7	1.7	1.7	1.7	1.6	1.6	1.6	1.5	1.5
Cowes I.o.W.	2.1	2.0	2.0	1.9	1.8	1.7	1.6	1.6	1.5	1.4	1.2	1.1
Sandown I.o.W.	1.9	1.8	1.8	1.7	1.7	1.6	1.5	1.4	1.3	1.2	1.2	1.1
Southampton	2.3	2.2	2.2	2.1	2.0	1.9	1.9	1.8	1.7	1.6	1.6	1.5
Portsmouth	2.1	2.0	2.0	1.9	1.8	1.7	1.6	1.5	1.4	1.4	1.3	1.3
Chichester entrance	2.0	1.9	1.9	1.8	1.7	1.7	1.6	1.6	1.5	1.5	1.4	1.4
Selsey Bill	2.1	2.0	1.8	1.7	1.6	1.5	1.4	1.3	1.2	1.1	1.1	1.0
Littlehampton Hbr	1.9	1.8	1.6	1.5	1.3	1.2	1.0	0.8	0.7	0.7	0.7	0.7
Littlehampton appr'ch	1.9	1.8	1.8	1.7	1.6	1.5	1.4	1.3	1.2	1.1	1.1	1.0
Shoreham	2.4	2.2	2.0	1.9	1.7	1.5	1.3	1.2	1.0	0.9	0.8	0.7
Brighton	2.4	2.2	2.1	1.8	1.7	1.5	1.3	1.2	1.0	0.9	0.7	0.6
Newhaven	2.4	2.2	2.0	1.8	1.6	1.4	1.2	1.0	0.8	0.7	0.5	0.4

PORTS, FRANCE

		4.8	5.0	5.2	5.4	5.6	5.8	6.0	6.2	6.4	6.6	6.8
Le Havre	4.1	3.9	3.7	3.5	3.3	3.1	2.9	2.7	2.5	2.3	2.2	2.0
Honfleur	4.1	3.9	3.7	3.5	3.3	3.1	2.9	2.7	2.5	2.4	2.3	2.2
Trouville (Deauville)	4.0	3.9	3.9	3.8	3.7	3.6	3.6	3.5	3.4	3.3	3.2	3.1
Ouistreham	4.1	4.0	3.8	3.7	3.6	3.5	3.3	3.2	3.1	3.0	2.9	2.8
Courseulles	3.6	3.7	3.9	4.0	4.1	4.3	4.4	4.6	4.7	4.7	4.8	4.8
Arromanches	4.3	4.4	4.4	4.5	4.5	4.6	4.6	4.7	4.7	4.7	4.7	4.7
Port-en-Bessin	4.1	4.1	4.1	4.1	4.1	4.1	4.1	4.1	4.1	4.0	4.0	3.9
Saint-Vaast-la-Hougue	3.8	3.7	3.7	3.6	3.6	3.5	3.5	3.4	3.4	3.3	3.3	3.2
Barfleur	3.9	3.9	3.9	3.9	3.9	3.9	3.9	3.9	3.9	3.9	3.9	3.9
Cherbourg	4.2	4.3	4.5	4.6	4.7	4.8	4.9	5.0	5.1	5.2	5.3	5.4
Omonville	4.3	4.4	4.6	4.7	4.8	4.9	5.1	5.2	5.4	5.6	5.7	
Goury	6.2	6.3	6.5	6.6	6.7	6.9	7.0	7.2	7.3	7.4	7.6	7.7
Dielette	6.7	7.0	7.4	7.7	8.0	8.3	8.6	8.9	9.2	9.4	9.7	9.9
Carteret	7.6	8.0	8.4	8.8	9.2	9.5	9.9	10.3	10.7	11.0	11.3	11.6
Granville	8.9	9.4	9.8	10.3	10.8	11.3	11.7	12.2	12.7	13.0	13.4	13.7
Saint Malo	8.4	8.9	9.3	9.8	10.2	10.7	11.1	11.6	12.0	12.3	12.6	12.9
All Hbrs, St Brieuc Bay	7.9	8.3	8.7	9.1	9.6	10.0	10.4	10.9	11.3	11.6	11.8	12.1
Paimpol	7.2	7.6	8.0	8.4	8.8	9.2	9.6	10.0	10.4	10.7	11.0	11.3
Ile de Bréhat	7.5	7.9	8.3	8.7	9.0	9.4	9.8	10.1	10.5	10.8	11.0	11.3
Lezardrieux	7.1	7.5	7.9	8.3	8.7	9.0	9.4	9.8	10.2	10.5	10.7	11.0

ISLANDS OFF

		4.8	5.0	5.2	5.4	5.6	5.8	6.0	6.2	6.4	6.6	6.8
Braye, Alderney	4.3	4.5	4.7	4.9	5.1	5.3	5.5	5.7	6.0	6.2	6.3	6.5
St Peter Port & Sark	6.2	6.5	6.9	7.2	7.5	7.8	8.2	8.5	8.8	9.0	9.3	9.5
St Helier, Jersey	7.5	7.9	8.3	8.7	9.2	9.6	10.0	10.5	10.9	11.3	11.6	12.0
St Catherine, Jersey	7.4	7.8	8.2	8.6	9.0	9.4	9.8	10.2	10.6	10.9	11.2	11.5
Les Minquiers	8.3	8.7	9.1	9.5	9.8	10.2	10.6	10.9	11.3	11.6	11.9	12.2
Iles Chausey	9.1	9.5	9.9	10.3	10.8	11.2	11.6	12.1	12.5	12.8	13.2	13.5

⇐ Coefficient de la marée ⇒

Scale: 30 40 50 60 70 80 90 100 110

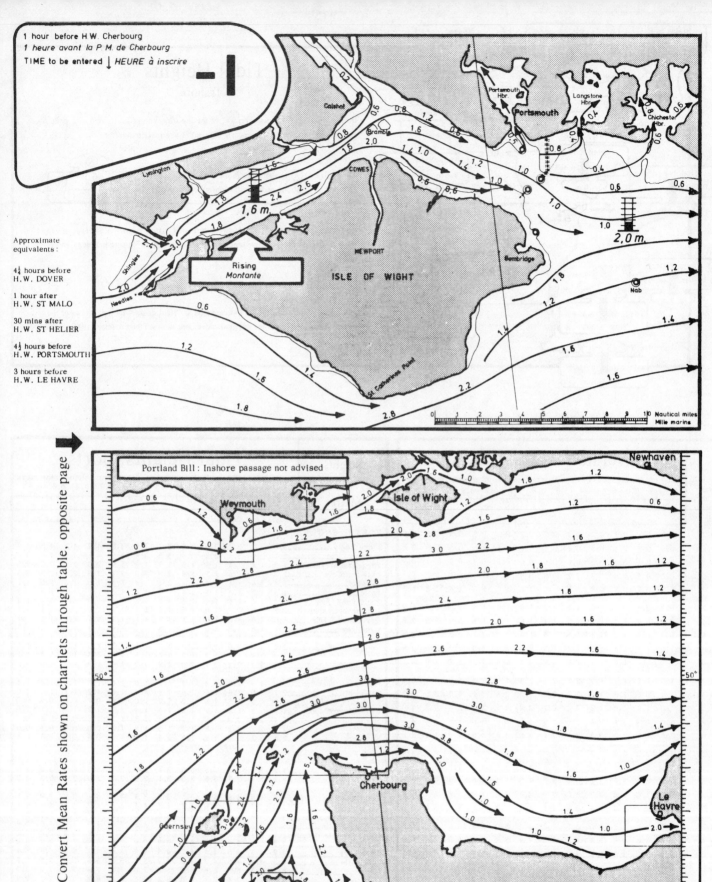

Calshot
Bramble
Lymington
COWES
NEWPORT
ISLE OF WIGHT
St. Catherines Point
Needles
Shingles

1.6 m
Rising
Montante

Portsmouth Hbr
Portsmouth
Langstone Hbr
Chichester Hbr
Bembridge
Nab

2.0 m

Approximate
equivalents :

4¼ hours before
H.W. DOVER

1 hour after
H.W. ST MALO

30 mins after
H.W. ST HELIER

4½ hours before
H.W. PORTSMOUTH

3 hours before
H.W. LE HAVRE

0   1   2   3   4   5   6   7   8   9   10   Nautical miles
                                                      Mille marins

Convert Mean Rates shown on chartlets through table, opposite page

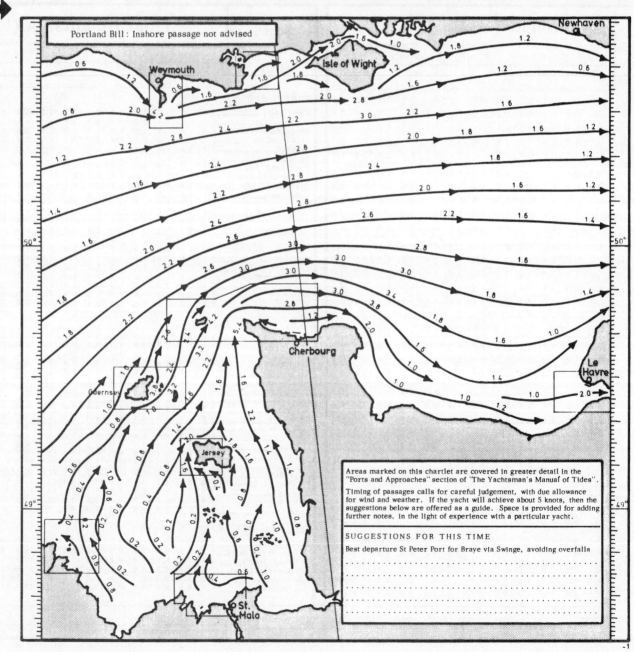

Portland Bill : Inshore passage not advised

Weymouth
Isle of Wight
Newhaven
Guernsey
Jersey
Cherbourg
Le Havre
St. Malo

50°
50°
49°
49°

Areas marked on this chartlet are covered in greater detail in the
"Ports and Approaches" section of 'The Yachtsman's Manual of Tides".

Timing of passages calls for careful judgement, with due allowance
for wind and weather. If the yacht will achieve about 5 knots, then the
suggestions below are offered as a guide. Space is provided for adding
further notes, in the light of experience with a particular yacht.

SUGGESTIONS FOR THIS TIME
Best departure St Peter Port for Braye via Swinge, avoiding overfalls
....
....
....
....
....

−1

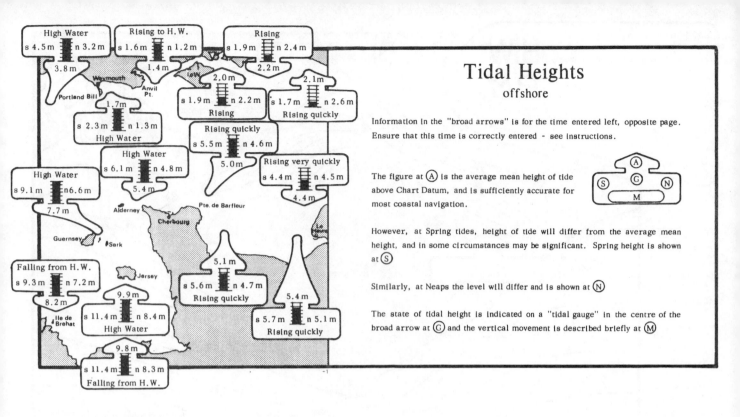

Tidal Heights
offshore

Information in the "broad arrows" is for the time entered left, opposite page. Ensure that this time is correctly entered - see instructions.

The figure at (A) is the average mean height of tide above Chart Datum, and is sufficiently accurate for most coastal navigation.

However, at Spring tides, height of tide will differ from the average mean height, and in some circumstances may be significant. Spring height is shown at (S)

Similarly, at Neaps the level will differ and is shown at (N)

The state of tidal height is indicated on a "tidal gauge" in the centre of the broad arrow at (G) and the vertical movement is described briefly at (M)

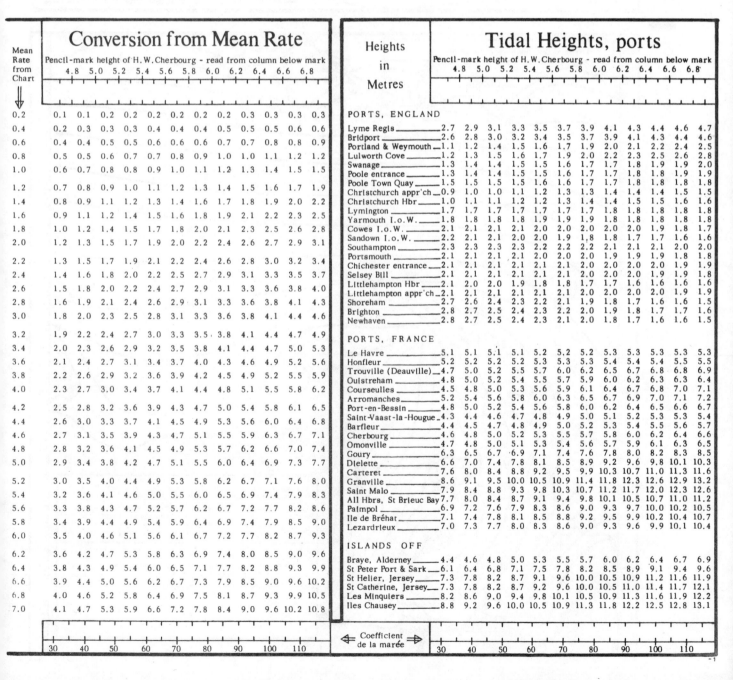

Conversion from Mean Rate

Pencil-mark height of H.W.Cherbourg - read from column below mark

Mean Rate from Chart ↓		4.8	5.0	5.2	5.4	5.6	5.8	6.0	6.2	6.4	6.6	6.8
0.2	0.1	0.1	0.2	0.2	0.2	0.2	0.2	0.2	0.3	0.3	0.3	0.3
0.4	0.2	0.3	0.3	0.3	0.4	0.4	0.4	0.5	0.5	0.5	0.6	0.6
0.6	0.4	0.4	0.5	0.5	0.6	0.6	0.6	0.7	0.7	0.8	0.8	0.9
0.8	0.5	0.5	0.6	0.7	0.7	0.8	0.9	1.0	1.0	1.1	1.2	1.2
1.0	0.6	0.7	0.8	0.8	0.9	1.0	1.1	1.2	1.3	1.4	1.5	1.5
1.2	0.7	0.8	0.9	1.0	1.1	1.2	1.3	1.4	1.5	1.6	1.7	1.9
1.4	0.8	0.9	1.1	1.2	1.3	1.4	1.6	1.7	1.8	1.9	2.0	2.2
1.6	0.9	1.1	1.2	1.4	1.5	1.6	1.8	1.9	2.1	2.2	2.3	2.5
1.8	1.0	1.2	1.4	1.5	1.7	1.8	2.0	2.1	2.3	2.5	2.6	2.8
2.0	1.2	1.3	1.5	1.7	1.9	2.0	2.2	2.4	2.6	2.7	2.9	3.1
2.2	1.3	1.5	1.7	1.9	2.1	2.2	2.4	2.6	2.8	3.0	3.2	3.4
2.4	1.4	1.6	1.8	2.0	2.2	2.5	2.7	2.9	3.1	3.3	3.5	3.7
2.6	1.5	1.8	2.0	2.2	2.4	2.7	2.9	3.1	3.3	3.6	3.8	4.0
2.8	1.6	1.9	2.1	2.4	2.6	2.9	3.1	3.3	3.6	3.8	4.1	4.3
3.0	1.8	2.0	2.3	2.5	2.8	3.1	3.3	3.6	3.8	4.1	4.4	4.6
3.2	1.9	2.2	2.4	2.7	3.0	3.3	3.5	3.8	4.1	4.4	4.7	4.9
3.4	2.0	2.3	2.6	2.9	3.2	3.5	3.8	4.1	4.4	4.7	5.0	5.3
3.6	2.1	2.4	2.7	3.1	3.4	3.7	4.0	4.3	4.6	4.9	5.2	5.6
3.8	2.2	2.6	2.9	3.2	3.6	3.9	4.2	4.5	4.9	5.2	5.5	5.9
4.0	2.3	2.7	3.0	3.4	3.7	4.1	4.4	4.8	5.1	5.5	5.8	6.2
4.2	2.5	2.8	3.2	3.6	3.9	4.3	4.7	5.0	5.4	5.8	6.1	6.5
4.4	2.6	3.0	3.3	3.7	4.1	4.5	4.9	5.3	5.6	6.0	6.4	6.8
4.6	2.7	3.1	3.5	3.9	4.3	4.7	5.1	5.5	5.9	6.3	6.7	7.1
4.8	2.8	3.2	3.6	4.1	4.5	4.9	5.3	5.7	6.2	6.6	7.0	7.4
5.0	2.9	3.4	3.8	4.2	4.7	5.1	5.5	6.0	6.4	6.9	7.3	7.7
5.2	3.0	3.5	4.0	4.4	4.9	5.3	5.8	6.2	6.7	7.1	7.6	8.0
5.4	3.2	3.6	4.1	4.6	5.0	5.5	6.0	6.5	6.9	7.4	7.9	8.3
5.6	3.3	3.8	4.3	4.7	5.2	5.7	6.2	6.7	7.2	7.7	8.2	8.6
5.8	3.4	3.9	4.4	4.9	5.4	5.9	6.4	6.9	7.4	7.9	8.5	9.0
6.0	3.5	4.0	4.6	5.1	5.6	6.1	6.7	7.2	7.7	8.2	8.7	9.3
6.2	3.6	4.2	4.7	5.3	5.8	6.3	6.9	7.4	8.0	8.5	9.0	9.6
6.4	3.8	4.3	4.9	5.4	6.0	6.5	7.1	7.7	8.2	8.8	9.3	9.9
6.6	3.9	4.4	5.0	5.6	6.2	6.7	7.3	7.9	8.5	9.0	9.6	10.2
6.8	4.0	4.6	5.2	5.8	6.4	6.9	7.5	8.1	8.7	9.3	9.9	10.5
7.0	4.1	4.7	5.3	5.9	6.6	7.2	7.8	8.4	9.0	9.6	10.2	10.8

Scale: 30 40 50 60 70 80 90 100 110

← Coefficient de la marée →

Tidal Heights, ports

Heights in Metres

Pencil-mark height of H.W.Cherbourg - read from column below mark

		4.8	5.0	5.2	5.4	5.6	5.8	6.0	6.2	6.4	6.6	6.8
PORTS, ENGLAND												
Lyme Regis	2.7	2.9	3.1	3.3	3.5	3.7	3.9	4.1	4.3	4.4	4.6	4.7
Bridport	2.6	2.8	3.0	3.2	3.4	3.5	3.7	3.9	4.1	4.3	4.4	4.6
Portland & Weymouth	1.1	1.2	1.4	1.5	1.6	1.7	1.9	2.0	2.1	2.2	2.4	2.5
Lulworth Cove	1.2	1.3	1.5	1.6	1.7	1.9	2.0	2.2	2.3	2.5	2.6	2.8
Swanage	1.3	1.4	1.4	1.5	1.5	1.6	1.7	1.7	1.8	1.9	1.9	2.0
Poole entrance	1.3	1.4	1.4	1.5	1.5	1.6	1.7	1.7	1.8	1.8	1.9	1.9
Poole Town Quay	1.5	1.5	1.5	1.5	1.6	1.6	1.7	1.7	1.8	1.8	1.8	1.8
Christchurch appr'ch	0.9	1.0	1.0	1.1	1.2	1.3	1.3	1.4	1.4	1.4	1.5	1.5
Christchurch Hbr	1.0	1.1	1.1	1.2	1.2	1.3	1.4	1.4	1.5	1.5	1.6	1.6
Lymington	1.7	1.7	1.7	1.7	1.7	1.7	1.7	1.8	1.8	1.8	1.8	1.8
Yarmouth I.o.W.	1.8	1.8	1.8	1.8	1.9	1.9	1.9	1.8	1.8	1.8	1.8	1.8
Cowes I.o.W.	2.1	2.1	2.1	2.1	2.0	2.0	2.0	2.0	2.0	1.9	1.8	1.7
Sandown I.o.W.	2.2	2.1	2.1	2.0	2.0	1.9	1.8	1.8	1.7	1.7	1.6	1.6
Southampton	2.3	2.3	2.3	2.3	2.2	2.2	2.2	2.1	2.1	2.1	2.0	2.0
Portsmouth	2.1	2.1	2.1	2.1	2.0	2.0	2.0	1.9	1.9	1.9	1.8	1.8
Chichester entrance	2.1	2.1	2.1	2.1	2.1	2.1	2.0	2.0	2.0	2.0	1.9	1.9
Selsey Bill	2.1	2.1	2.1	2.1	2.1	2.1	2.0	2.0	1.9	1.9	1.9	1.8
Littlehampton Hbr	2.1	2.0	2.0	1.9	1.8	1.8	1.7	1.7	1.6	1.6	1.6	1.6
Littlehampton appr'ch	2.1	2.1	2.1	2.1	2.1	2.1	2.0	2.0	2.0	2.0	1.9	1.9
Shoreham	2.7	2.6	2.4	2.3	2.2	2.1	1.9	1.8	1.7	1.6	1.6	1.5
Brighton	2.8	2.7	2.5	2.4	2.3	2.2	2.0	1.9	1.8	1.7	1.7	1.6
Newhaven	2.8	2.7	2.5	2.4	2.3	2.1	2.0	1.8	1.7	1.6	1.6	1.5
PORTS, FRANCE												
Le Havre	5.1	5.1	5.1	5.1	5.2	5.2	5.3	5.3	5.3	5.3	5.3	5.3
Honfleur	5.2	5.2	5.2	5.2	5.3	5.3	5.4	5.4	5.4	5.5	5.5	5.5
Trouville (Deauville)	4.7	5.0	5.2	5.5	5.7	6.0	6.2	6.5	6.7	6.8	6.8	6.9
Ouistreham	4.8	5.0	5.2	5.4	5.5	5.7	5.9	6.0	6.2	6.3	6.3	6.4
Courseulles	4.5	4.8	5.0	5.3	5.6	5.9	6.1	6.4	6.7	6.8	7.0	7.1
Arromanches	5.2	5.4	5.6	5.8	6.0	6.3	6.5	6.7	6.9	7.0	7.1	7.2
Port-en-Bessin	4.8	5.0	5.2	5.4	5.6	5.8	6.0	6.2	6.4	6.5	6.6	6.7
Saint-Vaast-la-Hougue	4.3	4.4	4.6	4.7	4.8	4.9	5.0	5.1	5.2	5.3	5.3	5.4
Barfleur	4.4	4.5	4.7	4.8	4.9	5.0	5.2	5.3	5.4	5.5	5.6	5.7
Cherbourg	4.6	4.8	5.0	5.2	5.3	5.5	5.7	5.8	6.0	6.2	6.4	6.6
Omonville	4.7	4.8	5.0	5.1	5.3	5.4	5.6	5.7	5.9	6.1	6.3	6.5
Goury	6.3	6.5	6.7	6.9	7.1	7.4	7.6	7.8	8.0	8.2	8.3	8.5
Dielette	6.6	7.0	7.4	7.8	8.1	8.5	8.9	9.2	9.6	9.8	10.1	10.3
Carteret	7.6	8.0	8.4	8.8	9.2	9.5	9.9	10.3	10.7	11.0	11.3	11.6
Granville	8.6	9.1	9.5	10.0	10.5	10.9	11.4	11.8	12.3	12.6	12.9	13.2
Saint Malo	7.9	8.4	8.8	9.3	9.8	10.3	10.7	11.2	11.7	12.0	12.3	12.6
All Hbrs, St Brieuc Bay	7.7	8.0	8.4	8.7	9.1	9.4	9.8	10.1	10.5	10.7	11.0	11.2
Paimpol	6.9	7.2	7.6	7.9	8.3	8.6	9.0	9.3	9.7	10.0	10.2	10.5
Ile de Bréhat	7.1	7.4	7.8	8.1	8.5	8.8	9.2	9.5	9.9	10.2	10.4	10.7
Lezardrieux	7.0	7.3	7.7	8.0	8.3	8.6	9.0	9.3	9.6	9.9	10.1	10.4
ISLANDS OFF												
Braye, Alderney	4.4	4.6	4.8	5.0	5.3	5.5	5.7	6.0	6.2	6.4	6.7	6.9
St Peter Port & Sark	6.1	6.4	6.8	7.1	7.5	7.8	8.2	8.5	8.9	9.1	9.4	9.6
St Helier, Jersey	7.3	7.8	8.2	8.7	9.1	9.6	10.0	10.5	10.9	11.2	11.6	11.9
St Catherine, Jersey	7.3	7.8	8.2	8.7	9.2	9.6	10.0	10.5	11.0	11.4	11.7	12.1
Les Minquiers	8.2	8.6	9.0	9.4	9.8	10.1	10.5	10.9	11.3	11.6	11.9	12.2
Iles Chausey	8.8	9.2	9.6	10.0	10.5	10.9	11.3	11.8	12.2	12.5	12.8	13.1

Scale: 30 40 50 60 70 80 90 100 110

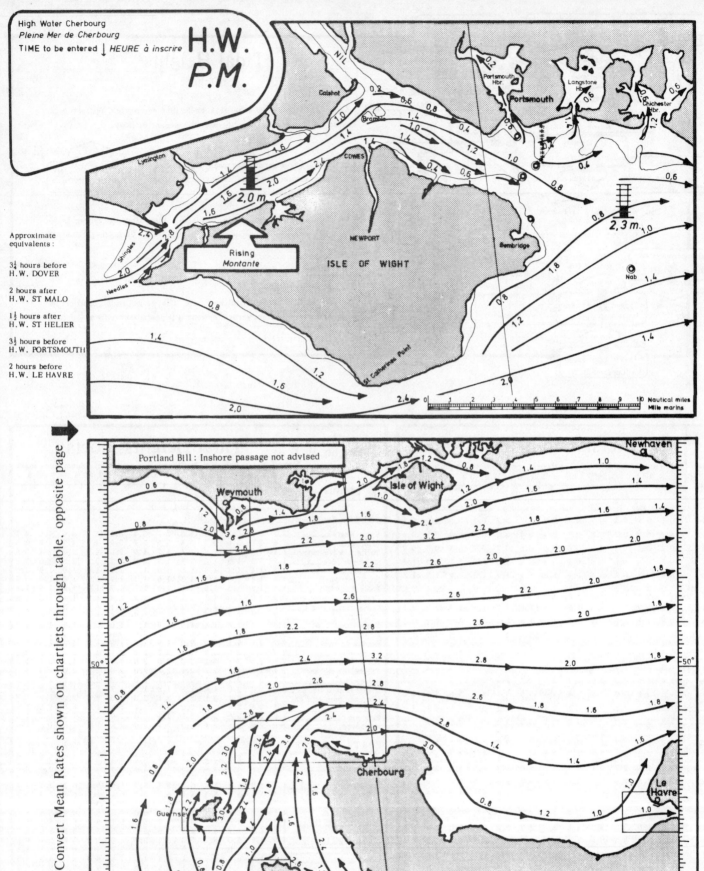

Approximate
equivalents :

3¼ hours before
H.W. DOVER

2 hours after
H.W. ST MALO

1½ hours after
H.W. ST HELIER

3½ hours before
H.W. PORTSMOUTH

2 hours before
H.W. LE HAVRE

Rising
Montante

ISLE OF WIGHT

Convert Mean Rates shown on chartlets through table, opposite page

Portland Bill : Inshore passage not advised

Areas marked on this chartlet are covered in greater detail in the "Ports and Approaches" section of "The Yachtsman's Manual of Tides".

Timing of passages calls for careful judgement, with due allowance for wind and weather. If the yacht will achieve about 5 knots, then the suggestions below are offered as a guide. Space is provided for adding further notes, in the light of experience with a particular yacht.

SUGGESTIONS FOR THIS TIME

Earliest departure Cherbourg for westward destinations via Alderney Race, using inshore eddies to Cap de la Hague

Depart Cherbourg for Braye, Alderney

. . . .

. . . .

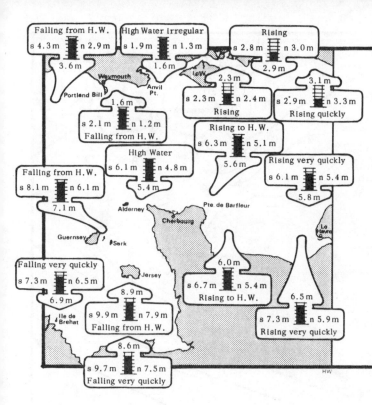

Tidal Heights
offshore

Information in the "broad arrows" is for the time entered left, opposite page. Ensure that this time is correctly entered - see instructions.

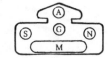

The figure at (A) is the average mean height of tide above Chart Datum, and is sufficiently accurate for most coastal navigation.

However, at Spring tides, height of tide will differ from the average mean height, and in some circumstances may be significant. Spring height is shown at (S)

Similarly, at Neaps the level will differ and is shown at (N)

The state of tidal height is indicated on a "tidal gauge" in the centre of the broad arrow at (G) and the vertical movement is described briefly at (M)

Conversion from Mean Rate

Pencil-mark height of H.W. Cherbourg - read from column below mark

Mean Rate from Chart ⇓		4.8	5.0	5.2	5.4	5.6	5.8	6.0	6.2	6.4	6.6	6.8
0.2	0.1	0.1	0.2	0.2	0.2	0.2	0.2	0.2	0.3	0.3	0.3	0.3
0.4	0.2	0.3	0.3	0.3	0.4	0.4	0.4	0.5	0.5	0.5	0.6	0.6
0.6	0.4	0.4	0.5	0.5	0.6	0.6	0.6	0.7	0.7	0.8	0.8	0.9
0.8	0.5	0.5	0.6	0.7	0.7	0.8	0.9	1.0	1.0	1.1	1.2	1.2
1.0	0.6	0.7	0.8	0.8	0.9	1.0	1.1	1.2	1.3	1.4	1.5	1.5
1.2	0.7	0.8	0.9	1.0	1.1	1.2	1.3	1.4	1.5	1.6	1.7	1.9
1.4	0.8	0.9	1.1	1.2	1.3	1.4	1.6	1.7	1.8	1.9	2.0	2.2
1.6	0.9	1.1	1.2	1.4	1.5	1.6	1.8	1.9	2.1	2.2	2.3	2.5
1.8	1.0	1.2	1.4	1.5	1.7	1.8	2.0	2.1	2.3	2.5	2.6	2.8
2.0	1.2	1.3	1.5	1.7	1.9	2.0	2.2	2.4	2.6	2.7	2.9	3.1
2.2	1.3	1.5	1.7	1.9	2.1	2.2	2.4	2.6	2.8	3.0	3.2	3.4
2.4	1.4	1.6	1.8	2.0	2.2	2.5	2.7	2.9	3.1	3.3	3.5	3.7
2.6	1.5	1.8	2.0	2.2	2.4	2.7	2.9	3.1	3.3	3.6	3.8	4.0
2.8	1.6	1.9	2.1	2.4	2.6	2.9	3.1	3.3	3.6	3.8	4.1	4.3
3.0	1.8	2.0	2.3	2.5	2.8	3.1	3.3	3.6	3.8	4.1	4.4	4.6
3.2	1.9	2.2	2.4	2.7	3.0	3.3	3.5	3.8	4.1	4.4	4.7	4.9
3.4	2.0	2.3	2.6	2.9	3.2	3.5	3.8	4.1	4.4	4.7	5.0	5.3
3.6	2.1	2.4	2.7	3.1	3.4	3.7	4.0	4.3	4.6	4.9	5.2	5.6
3.8	2.2	2.6	2.9	3.2	3.6	3.9	4.2	4.5	4.9	5.2	5.5	5.9
4.0	2.3	2.7	3.0	3.4	3.7	4.1	4.4	4.8	5.1	5.5	5.8	6.2
4.2	2.5	2.8	3.2	3.6	3.9	4.3	4.7	5.0	5.4	5.8	6.1	6.5
4.4	2.6	3.0	3.3	3.7	4.1	4.5	4.9	5.3	5.6	6.0	6.4	6.8
4.6	2.7	3.1	3.5	3.9	4.3	4.7	5.1	5.5	5.9	6.3	6.7	7.1
4.8	2.8	3.2	3.6	4.1	4.5	4.9	5.3	5.7	6.2	6.6	7.0	7.4
5.0	2.9	3.4	3.8	4.2	4.7	5.1	5.5	6.0	6.4	6.9	7.3	7.7
5.2	3.0	3.5	4.0	4.4	4.9	5.3	5.8	6.2	6.7	7.1	7.6	8.0
5.4	3.2	3.6	4.1	4.6	5.0	5.5	6.0	6.5	6.9	7.4	7.9	8.3
5.6	3.3	3.8	4.3	4.7	5.2	5.7	6.2	6.7	7.2	7.7	8.2	8.6
5.8	3.4	3.9	4.4	4.9	5.4	5.9	6.4	6.9	7.4	7.9	8.5	9.0
6.0	3.5	4.0	4.6	5.1	5.6	6.1	6.7	7.2	7.7	8.2	8.7	9.3
6.2	3.6	4.2	4.7	5.3	5.8	6.3	6.9	7.4	8.0	8.5	9.0	9.6
6.4	3.8	4.3	4.9	5.4	6.0	6.5	7.1	7.7	8.2	8.8	9.3	9.9
6.6	3.9	4.4	5.0	5.6	6.2	6.7	7.3	7.9	8.5	9.0	9.6	10.2
6.8	4.0	4.6	5.2	5.8	6.4	6.9	7.5	8.1	8.7	9.3	9.9	10.5
7.0	4.1	4.7	5.3	5.9	6.6	7.2	7.8	8.4	9.0	9.6	10.2	10.8

Scale: 30 40 50 60 70 80 90 100 110

Tidal Heights, ports

Heights in Metres

Pencil-mark height of H.W. Cherbourg - read from column below mark

		4.8	5.0	5.2	5.4	5.6	5.8	6.0	6.2	6.4	6.6	6.8
PORTS, ENGLAND												
Lyme Regis	3.8	3.9	3.9	4.0	4.0	4.1	4.1	4.2	4.2	4.3	4.5	4.6
Bridport	2.5	2.7	2.9	3.1	3.3	3.4	3.6	3.8	4.0	4.1	4.3	4.4
Portland & Weymouth	1.0	1.1	1.3	1.4	1.5	1.6	1.8	1.9	2.0	2.1	2.3	2.4
Lulworth Cove	1.1	1.2	1.4	1.5	1.6	1.7	1.9	2.0	2.1	2.3	2.4	2.6
Swanage	1.5	1.5	1.5	1.5	1.6	1.6	1.7	1.8	1.9	2.0	2.0	2.1
Poole entrance	1.3	1.4	1.4	1.5	1.5	1.6	1.7	1.9	2.0	2.0	2.1	2.1
Poole Town Quay	1.4	1.5	1.5	1.6	1.7	1.8	1.9	2.0	2.1	2.1	2.2	2.2
Christchurch appr'ch	1.0	1.1	1.1	1.2	1.3	1.4	1.5	1.6	1.7	1.7	1.8	1.8
Christchurch Hbr	1.1	1.2	1.2	1.3	1.4	1.5	1.6	1.6	1.7	1.7	1.8	1.8
Lymington	1.8	1.8	1.8	1.8	1.9	1.9	2.0	2.0	2.1	2.1	2.2	2.2
Yarmouth I.o.W.	1.8	1.9	1.9	2.0	2.0	2.1	2.1	2.1	2.1	2.1	2.2	2.2
Cowes I.o.W.	2.4	2.4	2.4	2.4	2.3	2.3	2.3	2.3	2.3	2.2	2.2	2.1
Sandown I.o.W.	2.4	2.4	2.4	2.4	2.3	2.3	2.3	2.3	2.3	2.3	2.3	2.3
Southampton	2.4	2.4	2.4	2.4	2.3	2.3	2.3	2.2	2.2	2.2	2.1	2.1
Portsmouth	2.4	2.4	2.4	2.4	2.3	2.3	2.3	2.2	2.2	2.2	2.2	2.2
Chichester entrance	2.4	2.4	2.4	2.4	2.4	2.4	2.4	2.4	2.4	2.4	2.3	2.3
Selsey Bill	2.4	2.4	2.4	2.4	2.4	2.4	2.4	2.3	2.3	2.3	2.3	2.2
Littlehampton Hbr	2.4	2.4	2.4	2.4	2.3	2.3	2.3	2.2	2.2	2.2	2.2	2.2
Littlehampton appr'ch	2.5	2.5	2.5	2.5	2.5	2.5	2.4	2.4	2.4	2.4	2.4	2.4
Shoreham	3.3	3.2	3.2	3.1	3.0	2.9	2.9	2.8	2.7	2.7	2.7	2.7
Brighton	3.3	3.3	3.3	3.2	3.2	3.1	3.1	3.0	3.0	3.0	2.9	2.9
Newhaven	3.4	3.3	3.3	3.2	3.1	3.1	3.0	3.0	2.9	2.9	2.9	2.9
PORTS, FRANCE												
Le Havre	5.7	5.9	6.1	6.3	6.4	6.6	6.8	7.0	7.1	7.2	7.3	7.4
Honfleur	6.2	6.3	6.5	6.6	6.7	6.9	7.0	7.2	7.3	7.4	7.5	7.6
Trouville (Deauville)	5.6	5.9	6.1	6.4	6.6	6.9	7.1	7.4	7.6	7.7	7.8	8.0
Ouistreham	5.6	5.8	6.0	6.2	6.4	6.7	6.9	7.1	7.3	7.4	7.5	7.6
Courseulles	5.2	5.4	5.6	5.8	6.1	6.3	6.5	6.8	7.0	7.2	7.4	7.5
Arromanches	5.7	5.9	6.1	6.3	6.5	6.8	7.0	7.2	7.4	7.5	7.7	7.8
Port-en-Bessin	5.4	5.6	5.8	6.0	6.2	6.4	6.6	6.8	7.0	7.1	7.2	7.3
Saint-Vaast-la-Hougue	4.9	5.1	5.3	5.5	5.6	5.8	6.0	6.1	6.3	6.5	6.6	6.8
Barfleur	4.8	5.0	5.2	5.4	5.5	5.7	5.9	6.0	6.2	6.4	6.5	6.7
Cherbourg	4.7	4.9	5.1	5.3	5.5	5.7	5.9	6.1	6.3	6.5	6.7	6.9
Omonville	4.7	4.9	5.1	5.3	5.5	5.6	5.8	6.0	6.2	6.4	6.7	6.9
Goury	6.0	6.2	6.4	6.6	6.8	7.1	7.3	7.5	7.7	7.9	8.0	8.2
Dielette	6.3	6.6	7.0	7.3	7.6	7.9	8.2	8.5	8.8	9.0	9.1	9.3
Carteret	7.3	7.6	7.8	8.1	8.4	8.7	9.0	9.3	9.6	9.8	10.0	10.2
Granville	7.8	8.2	8.6	9.0	9.3	9.7	10.0	10.4	10.8	11.0	11.2	11.4
Saint Malo	7.2	7.6	8.0	8.4	8.8	9.1	9.5	9.9	10.3	10.5	10.7	10.9
All Hbrs, St Brieuc Bay	6.9	7.2	7.4	7.7	7.9	8.2	8.4	8.7	8.9	9.0	9.2	9.3
Paimpol	6.2	6.4	6.6	6.8	7.1	7.3	7.5	7.8	8.0	8.2	8.3	8.5
Ile de Bréhat	6.3	6.6	6.8	7.1	7.4	7.8	8.0	8.3	8.6	8.7	8.9	9.0
Lezardrieux	5.9	6.2	6.4	6.7	6.9	7.2	7.4	7.7	7.9	8.1	8.2	8.4
ISLANDS OFF												
Braye, Alderney	4.3	4.5	4.7	4.9	5.1	5.3	5.5	5.7	5.9	6.1	6.4	6.6
St Peter Port & Sark	5.9	6.1	6.3	6.6	6.9	7.1	7.4	7.6	7.9	8.1	8.3	8.5
St Helier, Jersey	7.0	7.3	7.7	8.0	8.3	8.7	9.0	9.4	9.7	10.0	10.2	10.5
St Catherine, Jersey	7.0	7.4	7.8	8.2	8.5	8.9	9.3	9.6	10.0	10.3	10.5	10.8
Les Minquiers	7.9	8.2	8.4	8.7	9.0	9.3	9.6	9.9	10.2	10.4	10.6	10.8
Iles Chausey	8.1	8.4	8.8	9.1	9.4	9.7	10.1	10.4	10.7	10.9	11.1	11.3

⇐ Coefficient de la marée ⇒

Scale: 30 40 50 60 70 80 90 100 110

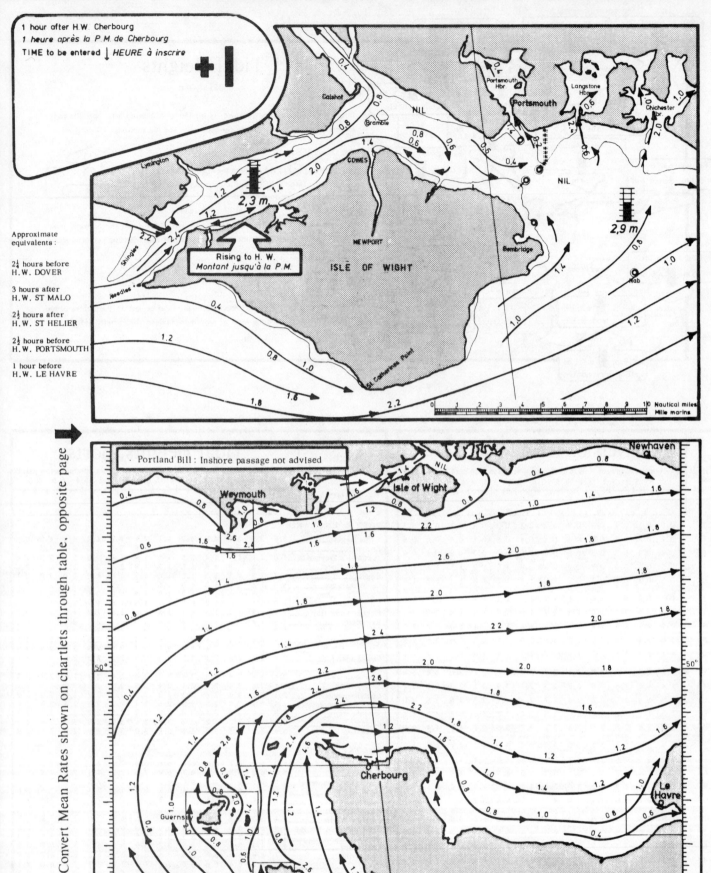

1 hour after H.W. Cherbourg
1 heure après la P.M. de Cherbourg
TIME to be entered ↓ *HEURE à inscrire*

+1

Approximate
equivalents :

2¼ hours before
H.W. DOVER

3 hours after
H.W. ST MALO

2½ hours after
H.W. ST HELIER

2½ hours before
H.W. PORTSMOUTH

1 hour before
H.W. LE HAVRE

Convert Mean Rates shown on chartlets through table, opposite page

Rising to H.W.
Montant jusqu'à la P.M.

2,3 m

2,9 m

NIL

ISLE OF WIGHT

Portsmouth

NEWPORT

COWES

Calshot

Bramble

Lymington

Shingles

Needles

St Catherine's Point

Nab

Bembridge

Langstone Hbr.

Chichester Hbr.

0 1 2 3 4 5 6 7 8 9 10 Nautical miles
Mile marins

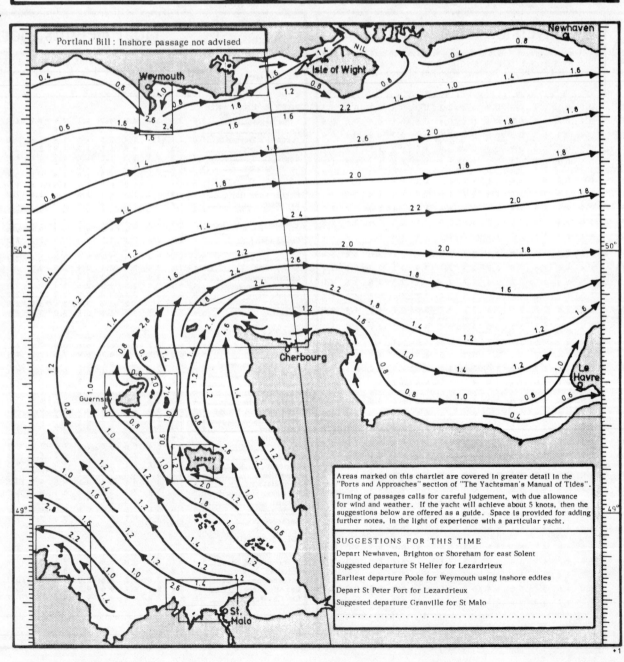

Portland Bill : Inshore passage not advised

Weymouth

Isle of Wight

Newhaven

Guernsey

Cherbourg

Jersey

St. Malo

Le Havre

50°

49°

Areas marked on this chartlet are covered in greater detail in the
"Ports and Approaches" section of "The Yachtsman's Manual of Tides".

Timing of passages calls for careful judgement, with due allowance
for wind and weather. If the yacht will achieve about 5 knots, then the
suggestions below are offered as a guide. Space is provided for adding
further notes, in the light of experience with a particular yacht.

SUGGESTIONS FOR THIS TIME
Depart Newhaven, Brighton or Shoreham for east Solent
Suggested departure St Helier for Lezardrieux
Earliest departure Poole for Weymouth using inshore eddies
Depart St Peter Port for Lezardrieux
Suggested departure Granville for St Malo
. . . .

•1

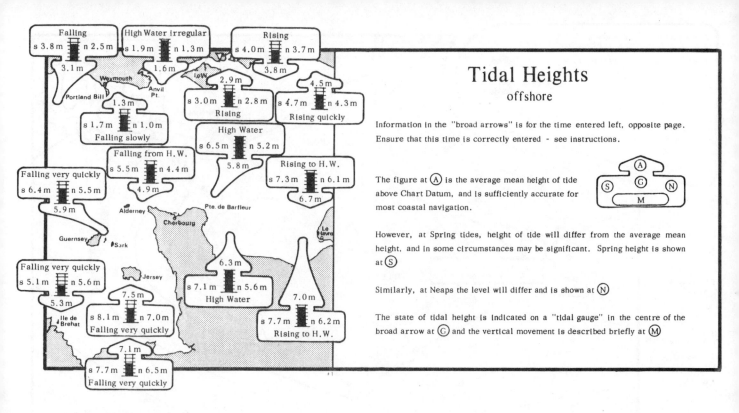

Tidal Heights
offshore

Information in the "broad arrows" is for the time entered left, opposite page. Ensure that this time is correctly entered - see instructions.

The figure at (A) is the average mean height of tide above Chart Datum, and is sufficiently accurate for most coastal navigation.

However, at Spring tides, height of tide will differ from the average mean height, and in some circumstances may be significant. Spring height is shown at (S)

Similarly, at Neaps the level will differ and is shown at (N)

The state of tidal height is indicated on a "tidal gauge" in the centre of the broad arrow at (G) and the vertical movement is described briefly at (M)

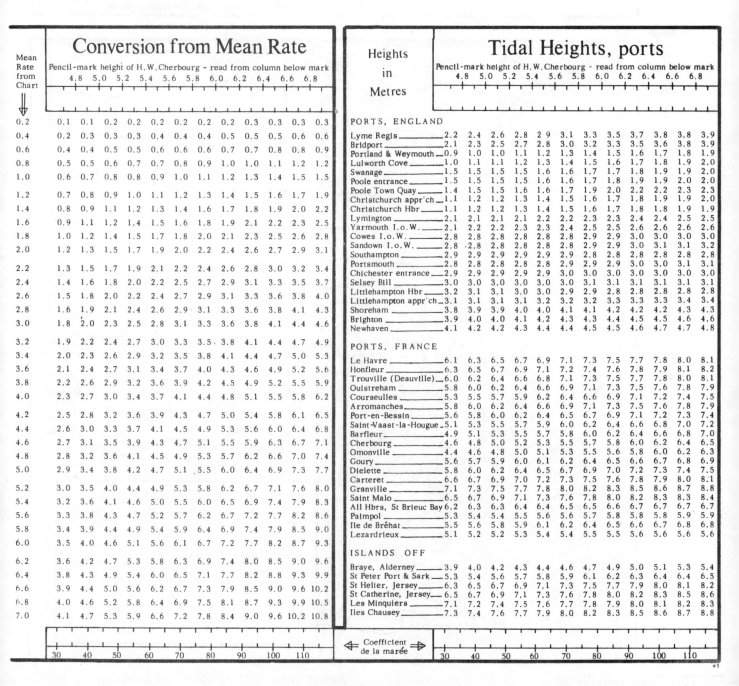

Conversion from Mean Rate

Pencil-mark height of H.W. Cherbourg - read from column below mark

Mean Rate from Chart		4.8	5.0	5.2	5.4	5.6	5.8	6.0	6.2	6.4	6.6	6.8
0.2	0.1	0.1	0.2	0.2	0.2	0.2	0.2	0.2	0.3	0.3	0.3	0.3
0.4	0.2	0.3	0.3	0.3	0.4	0.4	0.4	0.5	0.5	0.5	0.6	0.6
0.6	0.4	0.4	0.5	0.5	0.6	0.6	0.6	0.7	0.7	0.8	0.8	0.9
0.8	0.5	0.5	0.6	0.7	0.7	0.8	0.9	1.0	1.0	1.1	1.2	1.2
1.0	0.6	0.7	0.8	0.8	0.9	1.0	1.1	1.2	1.3	1.4	1.5	1.5
1.2	0.7	0.8	0.9	1.0	1.1	1.2	1.3	1.4	1.5	1.6	1.7	1.9
1.4	0.8	0.9	1.1	1.2	1.3	1.4	1.6	1.7	1.8	1.9	2.0	2.2
1.6	0.9	1.1	1.2	1.4	1.5	1.6	1.8	1.9	2.1	2.2	2.3	2.5
1.8	1.0	1.2	1.4	1.5	1.7	1.8	2.0	2.1	2.3	2.5	2.6	2.8
2.0	1.2	1.3	1.5	1.7	1.9	2.0	2.2	2.4	2.6	2.7	2.9	3.1
2.2	1.3	1.5	1.7	1.9	2.1	2.2	2.4	2.6	2.8	3.0	3.2	3.4
2.4	1.4	1.6	1.8	2.0	2.2	2.5	2.7	2.9	3.1	3.3	3.5	3.7
2.6	1.5	1.8	2.0	2.2	2.4	2.7	2.9	3.1	3.3	3.6	3.8	4.0
2.8	1.6	1.9	2.1	2.4	2.6	2.9	3.1	3.3	3.6	3.8	4.1	4.3
3.0	1.8	2.0	2.3	2.5	2.8	3.1	3.3	3.6	3.8	4.1	4.4	4.6
3.2	1.9	2.2	2.4	2.7	3.0	3.3	3.5	3.8	4.1	4.4	4.7	4.9
3.4	2.0	2.3	2.6	2.9	3.2	3.5	3.8	4.1	4.4	4.7	5.0	5.3
3.6	2.1	2.4	2.7	3.1	3.4	3.7	4.0	4.3	4.6	4.9	5.2	5.6
3.8	2.2	2.6	2.9	3.2	3.6	3.9	4.2	4.5	4.9	5.2	5.5	5.9
4.0	2.3	2.7	3.0	3.4	3.7	4.1	4.4	4.8	5.1	5.5	5.8	6.2
4.2	2.5	2.8	3.2	3.6	3.9	4.3	4.7	5.0	5.4	5.8	6.1	6.5
4.4	2.6	3.0	3.3	3.7	4.1	4.5	4.9	5.3	5.6	6.0	6.4	6.8
4.6	2.7	3.1	3.5	3.9	4.3	4.7	5.1	5.5	5.9	6.3	6.7	7.1
4.8	2.8	3.2	3.6	4.1	4.5	4.9	5.3	5.7	6.2	6.6	7.0	7.4
5.0	2.9	3.4	3.8	4.2	4.7	5.1	5.5	6.0	6.4	6.9	7.3	7.7
5.2	3.0	3.5	4.0	4.4	4.9	5.3	5.8	6.2	6.7	7.1	7.6	8.0
5.4	3.2	3.6	4.1	4.6	5.0	5.5	6.0	6.5	6.9	7.4	7.9	8.3
5.6	3.3	3.8	4.3	4.7	5.2	5.7	6.2	6.7	7.2	7.7	8.2	8.6
5.8	3.4	3.9	4.4	4.9	5.4	5.9	6.4	6.9	7.4	7.9	8.5	9.0
6.0	3.5	4.0	4.6	5.1	5.6	6.1	6.7	7.2	7.7	8.2	8.7	9.3
6.2	3.6	4.2	4.7	5.3	5.8	6.3	6.9	7.4	8.0	8.5	9.0	9.6
6.4	3.8	4.3	4.9	5.4	6.0	6.5	7.1	7.7	8.2	8.8	9.3	9.9
6.6	3.9	4.4	5.0	5.6	6.2	6.7	7.3	7.9	8.5	9.0	9.6	10.2
6.8	4.0	4.6	5.2	5.8	6.4	6.9	7.5	8.1	8.7	9.3	9.9	10.5
7.0	4.1	4.7	5.3	5.9	6.6	7.2	7.8	8.4	9.0	9.6	10.2	10.8

Tidal Heights, ports

Heights in Metres

Pencil-mark height of H.W. Cherbourg - read from column below mark

		4.8	5.0	5.2	5.4	5.6	5.8	6.0	6.2	6.4	6.6	6.8
PORTS, ENGLAND												
Lyme Regis	2.2	2.4	2.6	2.8	2.9	3.1	3.3	3.5	3.7	3.8	3.8	3.9
Bridport	2.1	2.3	2.5	2.7	2.8	3.0	3.2	3.3	3.5	3.6	3.8	3.9
Portland & Weymouth	0.9	1.0	1.0	1.1	1.2	1.3	1.4	1.5	1.6	1.7	1.8	1.9
Lulworth Cove	1.0	1.1	1.1	1.2	1.3	1.4	1.5	1.6	1.7	1.8	1.9	2.0
Swanage	1.5	1.5	1.5	1.5	1.6	1.6	1.7	1.7	1.8	1.9	1.9	2.0
Poole entrance	1.5	1.5	1.5	1.5	1.6	1.6	1.7	1.8	1.9	1.9	2.0	2.0
Poole Town Quay	1.4	1.5	1.5	1.6	1.6	1.7	1.9	2.0	2.2	2.2	2.3	2.3
Christchurch appr'ch	1.1	1.2	1.2	1.3	1.4	1.5	1.6	1.7	1.8	1.9	1.9	2.0
Christchurch Hbr	1.1	1.2	1.2	1.3	1.4	1.5	1.6	1.7	1.8	1.8	1.9	1.9
Lymington	2.1	2.1	2.1	2.1	2.2	2.2	2.3	2.3	2.4	2.4	2.5	2.5
Yarmouth I.o.W.	2.1	2.2	2.2	2.3	2.3	2.4	2.5	2.5	2.6	2.6	2.6	2.6
Cowes I.o.W.	2.8	2.8	2.8	2.8	2.8	2.8	2.9	2.9	3.0	3.0	3.0	3.0
Sandown I.o.W.	2.8	2.8	2.8	2.8	2.8	2.8	2.9	2.9	3.0	3.1	3.1	3.2
Southampton	2.9	2.9	2.9	2.9	2.9	2.9	2.8	2.8	2.8	2.8	2.8	2.8
Portsmouth	2.8	2.8	2.8	2.8	2.8	2.9	2.9	2.9	3.0	3.0	3.1	3.1
Chichester entrance	2.9	2.9	2.9	2.9	2.9	3.0	3.0	3.0	3.0	3.0	3.0	3.0
Selsey Bill	3.0	3.0	3.0	3.0	3.0	3.0	3.1	3.1	3.1	3.1	3.1	3.1
Littlehampton Hbr	3.2	3.1	3.1	3.0	3.0	2.9	2.9	2.8	2.8	2.8	2.8	2.8
Littlehampton appr'ch	3.1	3.1	3.1	3.1	3.2	3.2	3.2	3.3	3.3	3.3	3.4	3.4
Shoreham	3.8	3.9	3.9	4.0	4.0	4.1	4.1	4.2	4.2	4.2	4.3	4.3
Brighton	3.9	4.0	4.0	4.1	4.2	4.3	4.3	4.4	4.5	4.5	4.6	4.6
Newhaven	4.1	4.2	4.2	4.3	4.4	4.4	4.5	4.5	4.6	4.7	4.7	4.8
PORTS, FRANCE												
Le Havre	6.1	6.3	6.5	6.7	6.9	7.1	7.3	7.5	7.7	7.8	8.0	8.1
Honfleur	6.3	6.5	6.7	6.9	7.1	7.2	7.4	7.6	7.8	7.9	8.1	8.2
Trouville (Deauville)	6.0	6.2	6.4	6.6	6.8	7.1	7.3	7.5	7.7	7.8	8.0	8.1
Ouistreham	5.8	6.0	6.2	6.4	6.6	6.9	7.1	7.3	7.5	7.6	7.8	7.9
Courseulles	5.3	5.5	5.7	5.9	6.2	6.4	6.6	6.9	7.1	7.2	7.4	7.5
Arromanches	5.8	6.0	6.2	6.4	6.6	6.9	7.1	7.3	7.5	7.6	7.8	7.9
Port-en-Bessin	5.6	5.8	6.0	6.2	6.4	6.5	6.7	6.9	7.1	7.2	7.3	7.4
Saint-Vaast-la-Hougue	5.1	5.3	5.5	5.7	5.9	6.0	6.2	6.4	6.6	6.8	7.0	7.2
Barfleur	4.9	5.1	5.3	5.5	5.7	5.8	6.0	6.2	6.4	6.6	6.8	7.0
Cherbourg	4.6	4.8	5.0	5.2	5.3	5.5	5.7	5.8	6.0	6.2	6.4	6.5
Omonville	4.4	4.6	4.8	5.0	5.1	5.3	5.5	5.6	5.8	6.0	6.2	6.3
Goury	5.6	5.7	5.9	6.0	6.1	6.2	6.4	6.5	6.6	6.7	6.8	6.9
Dielette	5.8	6.0	6.2	6.4	6.5	6.7	6.9	7.0	7.2	7.3	7.4	7.5
Carteret	6.6	6.7	6.9	7.0	7.2	7.3	7.5	7.6	7.8	7.9	8.0	8.1
Granville	7.1	7.3	7.5	7.7	7.8	8.0	8.2	8.3	8.5	8.6	8.7	8.8
Saint Malo	6.5	6.7	6.9	7.1	7.3	7.6	7.8	8.0	8.2	8.3	8.3	8.4
All Hbrs, St Brieuc Bay	6.2	6.3	6.3	6.4	6.4	6.5	6.5	6.6	6.7	6.7	6.7	6.7
Paimpol	5.3	5.4	5.4	5.5	5.6	5.6	5.7	5.8	5.8	5.8	5.9	5.9
Ile de Bréhat	5.5	5.6	5.8	5.9	6.1	6.2	6.4	6.5	6.6	6.7	6.8	6.8
Lezardrieux	5.1	5.2	5.2	5.3	5.4	5.4	5.5	5.5	5.6	5.6	5.6	5.6
ISLANDS OFF												
Braye, Alderney	3.9	4.0	4.2	4.3	4.4	4.6	4.7	4.9	5.0	5.1	5.3	5.4
St Peter Port & Sark	5.3	5.4	5.6	5.7	5.8	5.9	6.1	6.2	6.3	6.4	6.4	6.5
St Helier, Jersey	6.3	6.5	6.7	6.9	7.1	7.3	7.5	7.7	7.9	8.0	8.1	8.2
St Catherine, Jersey	6.5	6.7	6.9	7.1	7.3	7.6	7.8	8.0	8.2	8.3	8.5	8.6
Les Minquiers	7.1	7.2	7.4	7.5	7.6	7.7	7.8	7.9	8.0	8.1	8.2	8.3
Iles Chausey	7.3	7.4	7.6	7.7	7.9	8.0	8.2	8.3	8.5	8.6	8.7	8.8

Coefficient de la marée

Scale: 30 40 50 60 70 80 90 100 110

+1

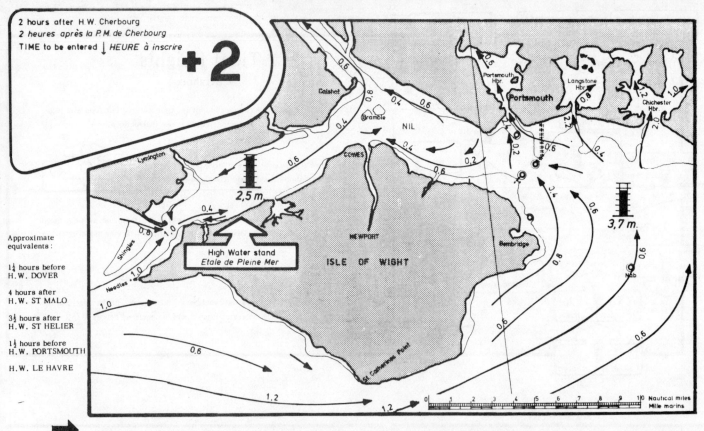

2 hours after H.W. Cherbourg
2 heures après la P.M. de Cherbourg
TIME to be entered ↓ *HEURE à inscrire*

+2

Approximate
equivalents :

1¼ hours before
H.W. DOVER

4 hours after
H.W. ST MALO

3½ hours after
H.W. ST HELIER

1½ hours before
H.W. PORTSMOUTH

H.W. LE HAVRE

2,5 m.

High Water stand
Etale de Pleine Mer

ISLE OF WIGHT

3,7 m.

Convert Mean Rates shown on chartlets through table, opposite page

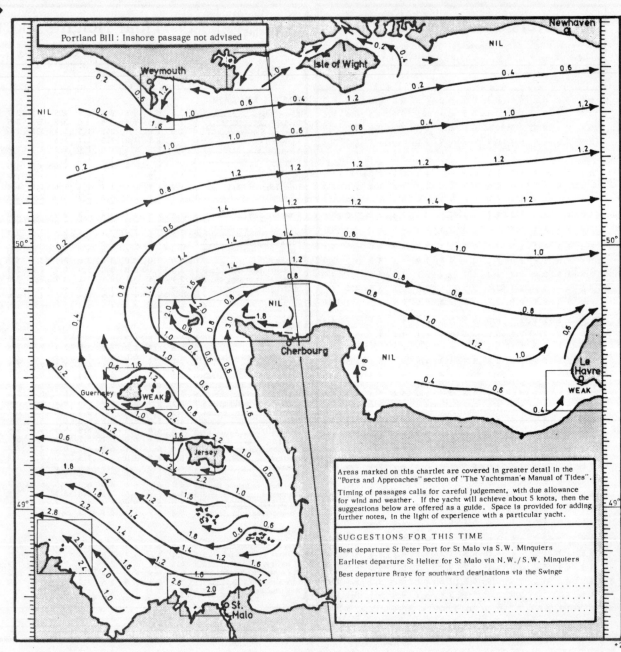

Portland Bill : Inshore passage not advised

Areas marked on this chartlet are covered in greater detail in the
"Ports and Approaches" section of "The Yachtsman's Manual of Tides".

Timing of passages calls for careful judgement, with due allowance
for wind and weather. If the yacht will achieve about 5 knots, then the
suggestions below are offered as a guide. Space is provided for adding
further notes, in the light of experience with a particular yacht.

SUGGESTIONS FOR THIS TIME

Best departure St Peter Port for St Malo via S.W. Minquiers
Earliest departure St Helier for St Malo via N.W./S.W. Minquiers
Best departure Brave for southward destinations via the Swinge

• •

• •

• •

*2

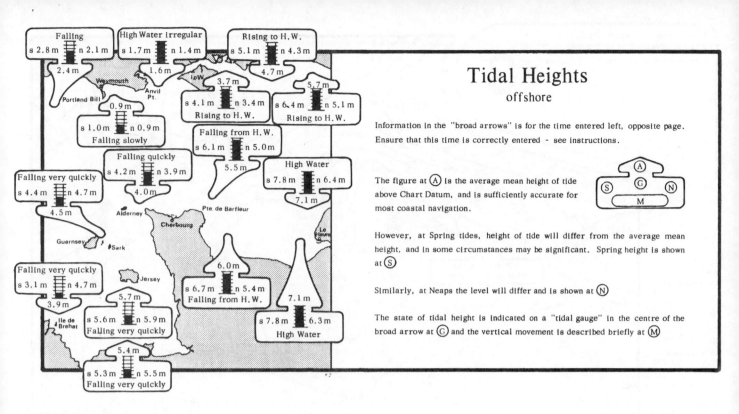

Tidal Heights
offshore

Information in the "broad arrows" is for the time entered left, opposite page. Ensure that this time is correctly entered - see instructions.

The figure at (A) is the average mean height of tide above Chart Datum, and is sufficiently accurate for most coastal navigation.

However, at Spring tides, height of tide will differ from the average mean height, and in some circumstances may be significant. Spring height is shown at (S)

Similarly, at Neaps the level will differ and is shown at (N)

The state of tidal height is indicated on a "tidal gauge" in the centre of the broad arrow at (G) and the vertical movement is described briefly at (M)

Offshore broad-arrow readings (selected):
- Falling — s 2.8m n 2.1m — 2.4m
- High Water Irregular — s 1.7m n 1.4m — 1.6m
- Rising to H.W. — s 5.1m n 4.3m — 4.7m
- Rising to H.W. — s 4.1m n 3.4m — 3.7m
- Rising to H.W. — s 6.4m n 5.1m — 5.7m
- Falling slowly — s 1.0m n 0.9m — 0.9m
- Falling from H.W. — s 6.1m n 5.0m — 5.5m
- Falling quickly — s 4.2m n 3.9m — 4.0m
- High Water — s 7.8m n 6.4m — 7.1m
- Falling very quickly — s 4.4m n 4.7m — 4.5m
- Falling very quickly — s 3.1m n 4.7m — 3.9m
- Falling from H.W. — s 6.7m n 5.4m — 6.0m
- High Water — s 7.8m n 6.3m — 7.1m
- Falling very quickly — s 5.6m n 5.9m — 5.7m
- Falling very quickly — s 5.3m n 5.5m — 5.4m

Map labels: Weymouth, Portland Bill, Anvil Pt., IoW, Alderney, Guernsey, Sark, Jersey, Cherbourg, Pte. de Barfleur, Le Havre, Ile de Bréhat

---

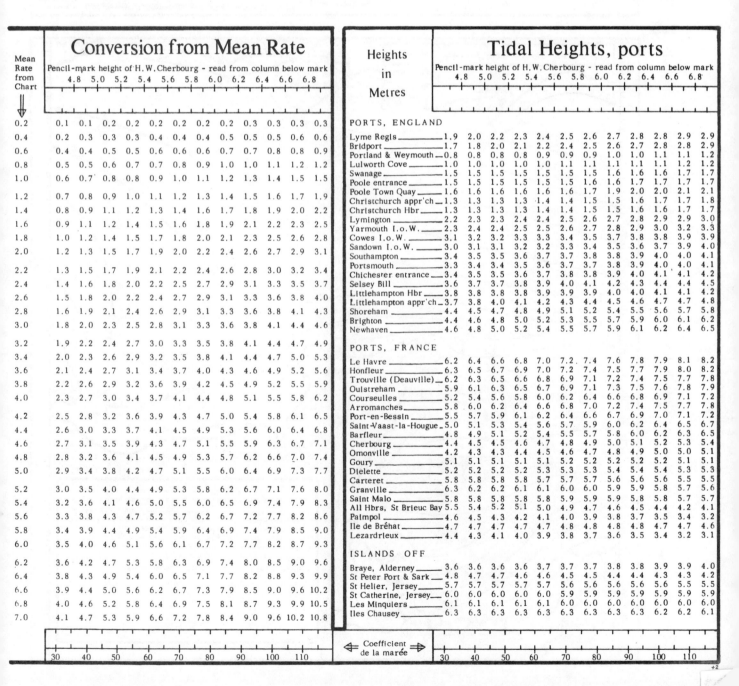

Conversion from Mean Rate

Pencil-mark height of H.W. Cherbourg - read from column below mark

Mean Rate from Chart	4.8	5.0	5.2	5.4	5.6	5.8	6.0	6.2	6.4	6.6	6.8	
0.2	0.1	0.1	0.2	0.2	0.2	0.2	0.2	0.2	0.3	0.3	0.3	0.3
0.4	0.2	0.3	0.3	0.3	0.4	0.4	0.4	0.5	0.5	0.5	0.6	0.6
0.6	0.4	0.4	0.5	0.5	0.6	0.6	0.6	0.7	0.7	0.8	0.8	0.9
0.8	0.5	0.5	0.6	0.7	0.7	0.8	0.9	1.0	1.0	1.1	1.2	1.2
1.0	0.6	0.7	0.8	0.8	0.9	1.0	1.1	1.2	1.3	1.4	1.5	1.5
1.2	0.7	0.8	0.9	1.0	1.1	1.2	1.3	1.4	1.5	1.6	1.7	1.9
1.4	0.8	0.9	1.1	1.2	1.3	1.4	1.6	1.7	1.8	1.9	2.0	2.2
1.6	0.9	1.1	1.2	1.4	1.5	1.6	1.8	1.9	2.1	2.2	2.3	2.5
1.8	1.0	1.2	1.4	1.5	1.7	1.8	2.0	2.1	2.3	2.5	2.6	2.8
2.0	1.2	1.3	1.5	1.7	1.9	2.0	2.2	2.4	2.6	2.7	2.9	3.1
2.2	1.3	1.5	1.7	1.9	2.1	2.2	2.4	2.6	2.8	3.0	3.2	3.4
2.4	1.4	1.6	1.8	2.0	2.2	2.5	2.7	2.9	3.1	3.3	3.5	3.7
2.6	1.5	1.8	2.0	2.2	2.4	2.7	2.9	3.1	3.3	3.6	3.8	4.0
2.8	1.6	1.9	2.1	2.4	2.6	2.9	3.1	3.3	3.6	3.8	4.1	4.3
3.0	1.8	2.0	2.3	2.5	2.8	3.1	3.3	3.6	3.8	4.1	4.4	4.6
3.2	1.9	2.2	2.4	2.7	3.0	3.3	3.5	3.8	4.1	4.4	4.7	4.9
3.4	2.0	2.3	2.6	2.9	3.2	3.5	3.8	4.1	4.4	4.7	5.0	5.3
3.6	2.1	2.4	2.7	3.1	3.4	3.7	4.0	4.3	4.6	4.9	5.2	5.6
3.8	2.2	2.6	2.9	3.2	3.6	3.9	4.2	4.5	4.9	5.2	5.5	5.9
4.0	2.3	2.7	3.0	3.4	3.7	4.1	4.4	4.8	5.1	5.5	5.8	6.2
4.2	2.5	2.8	3.2	3.6	3.9	4.3	4.7	5.0	5.4	5.8	6.1	6.5
4.4	2.6	3.0	3.3	3.7	4.1	4.5	4.9	5.3	5.6	6.0	6.4	6.8
4.6	2.7	3.1	3.5	3.9	4.3	4.7	5.1	5.5	5.9	6.3	6.7	7.1
4.8	2.8	3.2	3.6	4.1	4.5	4.9	5.3	5.7	6.2	6.6	7.0	7.4
5.0	2.9	3.4	3.8	4.2	4.7	5.1	5.5	6.0	6.4	6.9	7.3	7.7
5.2	3.0	3.5	4.0	4.4	4.9	5.3	5.8	6.2	6.7	7.1	7.6	8.0
5.4	3.2	3.6	4.1	4.6	5.0	5.5	6.0	6.5	6.9	7.4	7.9	8.3
5.6	3.3	3.8	4.3	4.7	5.2	5.7	6.2	6.7	7.2	7.7	8.2	8.6
5.8	3.4	3.9	4.4	4.9	5.4	5.9	6.4	6.9	7.4	7.9	8.5	9.0
6.0	3.5	4.0	4.6	5.1	5.6	6.1	6.7	7.2	7.7	8.2	8.7	9.3
6.2	3.6	4.2	4.7	5.3	5.8	6.3	6.9	7.4	8.0	8.5	9.0	9.6
6.4	3.8	4.3	4.9	5.4	6.0	6.5	7.1	7.7	8.2	8.8	9.3	9.9
6.6	3.9	4.4	5.0	5.6	6.2	6.7	7.3	7.9	8.5	9.0	9.6	10.2
6.8	4.0	4.6	5.2	5.8	6.4	6.9	7.5	8.1	8.7	9.3	9.9	10.5
7.0	4.1	4.7	5.3	5.9	6.6	7.2	7.8	8.4	9.0	9.6	10.2	10.8

Coefficient scale: 30 40 50 60 70 80 90 100 110

Tidal Heights, ports

Heights in Metres

Pencil-mark height of H.W. Cherbourg - read from column below mark

	4.8	5.0	5.2	5.4	5.6	5.8	6.0	6.2	6.4	6.6	6.8	
PORTS, ENGLAND												
Lyme Regis	1.9	2.0	2.2	2.3	2.4	2.5	2.6	2.7	2.8	2.8	2.9	2.9
Bridport	1.7	1.8	2.0	2.1	2.2	2.4	2.5	2.6	2.7	2.8	2.8	2.9
Portland & Weymouth	0.8	0.8	0.8	0.8	0.9	0.9	0.9	1.0	1.0	1.1	1.1	1.2
Lulworth Cove	1.0	1.0	1.0	1.0	1.0	1.1	1.1	1.1	1.1	1.1	1.2	1.2
Swanage	1.5	1.5	1.5	1.5	1.5	1.5	1.5	1.6	1.6	1.6	1.7	1.7
Poole entrance	1.5	1.5	1.5	1.5	1.5	1.5	1.6	1.6	1.7	1.7	1.7	1.7
Poole Town Quay	1.6	1.6	1.6	1.6	1.6	1.6	1.7	1.9	2.0	2.0	2.1	2.1
Christchurch appr'ch	1.3	1.3	1.3	1.3	1.4	1.4	1.5	1.5	1.6	1.7	1.7	1.8
Christchurch Hbr	1.3	1.3	1.3	1.3	1.4	1.4	1.5	1.5	1.6	1.6	1.7	1.7
Lymington	2.2	2.3	2.3	2.4	2.4	2.5	2.6	2.7	2.8	2.9	2.9	3.0
Yarmouth I.o.W.	2.3	2.4	2.4	2.5	2.5	2.6	2.7	2.8	2.9	3.0	3.2	3.3
Cowes I.o.W.	3.1	3.2	3.2	3.3	3.3	3.4	3.5	3.7	3.8	3.8	3.9	3.9
Sandown I.o.W.	3.0	3.1	3.1	3.2	3.2	3.3	3.4	3.5	3.6	3.7	3.9	4.0
Southampton	3.4	3.5	3.5	3.6	3.7	3.7	3.8	3.8	3.9	4.0	4.0	4.1
Portsmouth	3.3	3.4	3.4	3.5	3.6	3.7	3.7	3.8	3.9	4.0	4.0	4.1
Chichester entrance	3.4	3.5	3.5	3.6	3.7	3.8	3.8	3.9	4.0	4.1	4.1	4.3
Selsey Bill	3.6	3.7	3.7	3.8	3.9	4.0	4.1	4.2	4.3	4.4	4.4	4.5
Littlehampton Hbr	3.8	3.8	3.8	3.8	3.9	3.9	3.9	4.0	4.0	4.1	4.1	4.2
Littlehampton appr'ch	3.7	3.8	4.0	4.1	4.2	4.3	4.4	4.5	4.6	4.7	4.7	4.8
Shoreham	4.4	4.5	4.7	4.8	4.9	5.1	5.2	5.4	5.5	5.6	5.7	5.8
Brighton	4.4	4.6	4.8	5.0	5.2	5.3	5.5	5.7	5.9	6.0	6.1	6.2
Newhaven	4.6	4.8	5.0	5.2	5.4	5.5	5.7	5.9	6.1	6.2	6.4	6.5
PORTS, FRANCE												
Le Havre	6.2	6.4	6.6	6.8	7.0	7.2	7.4	7.6	7.8	7.9	8.1	8.2
Honfleur	6.3	6.5	6.7	6.9	7.0	7.2	7.4	7.5	7.7	7.9	8.0	8.2
Trouville (Deauville)	6.2	6.3	6.5	6.6	6.8	6.9	7.1	7.2	7.4	7.5	7.7	7.8
Ouistreham	5.9	6.1	6.3	6.5	6.7	6.9	7.1	7.3	7.5	7.6	7.8	7.9
Courseulles	5.2	5.4	5.6	5.8	6.0	6.2	6.4	6.6	6.8	6.9	7.1	7.2
Arromanches	5.8	6.0	6.2	6.4	6.6	6.8	7.0	7.2	7.4	7.5	7.7	7.8
Port-en-Bessin	5.5	5.7	5.9	6.1	6.2	6.4	6.6	6.7	6.9	7.0	7.1	7.2
Saint-Vaast-la-Hougue	5.0	5.1	5.3	5.4	5.6	5.7	5.9	6.0	6.2	6.4	6.5	6.7
Barfleur	4.8	4.9	5.1	5.2	5.4	5.5	5.7	5.8	6.0	6.2	6.3	6.5
Cherbourg	4.4	4.5	4.5	4.6	4.7	4.8	4.9	5.0	5.1	5.2	5.3	5.4
Omonville	4.2	4.3	4.3	4.4	4.5	4.6	4.7	4.8	4.9	5.0	5.0	5.1
Goury	5.1	5.1	5.1	5.1	5.1	5.2	5.2	5.2	5.2	5.2	5.1	5.1
Dielette	5.2	5.2	5.2	5.2	5.3	5.3	5.3	5.4	5.4	5.4	5.3	5.3
Carteret	5.8	5.8	5.8	5.8	5.7	5.7	5.7	5.6	5.6	5.6	5.5	5.5
Granville	6.3	6.2	6.2	6.1	6.1	6.0	6.0	5.9	5.9	5.8	5.7	5.6
Saint Malo	5.8	5.8	5.8	5.8	5.8	5.9	5.9	5.9	5.8	5.8	5.7	5.7
All Hbrs, St Brieuc Bay	5.5	5.4	5.2	5.1	5.0	4.9	4.7	4.6	4.5	4.4	4.2	4.1
Paimpol	4.6	4.5	4.3	4.2	4.1	4.0	3.9	3.8	3.7	3.5	3.4	3.2
Ile de Bréhat	4.7	4.7	4.7	4.7	4.7	4.8	4.8	4.8	4.8	4.7	4.7	4.6
Lezardrieux	4.4	4.3	4.1	4.0	3.9	3.8	3.7	3.6	3.5	3.4	3.2	3.1
ISLANDS OFF												
Braye, Alderney	3.6	3.6	3.6	3.6	3.7	3.7	3.7	3.8	3.8	3.9	3.9	4.0
St Peter Port & Sark	4.8	4.7	4.7	4.6	4.6	4.5	4.5	4.4	4.4	4.3	4.3	4.2
St Helier, Jersey	5.7	5.7	5.7	5.7	5.7	5.6	5.6	5.6	5.6	5.6	5.5	5.5
St Catherine, Jersey	6.0	6.0	6.0	6.0	6.0	5.9	5.9	5.9	5.9	5.9	5.9	5.9
Les Minquiers	6.1	6.1	6.1	6.1	6.1	6.0	6.0	6.0	6.0	6.0	6.0	6.0
Iles Chausey	6.3	6.3	6.3	6.3	6.3	6.3	6.3	6.3	6.3	6.2	6.2	6.1

Coefficient de la marée: 30 40 50 60 70 80 90 100 110

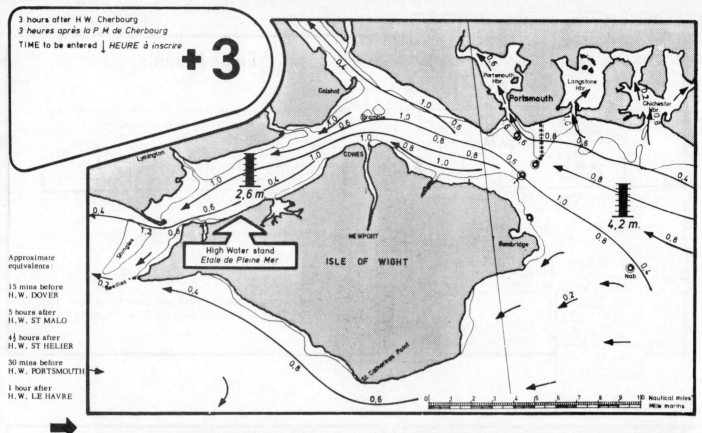

High Water stand
Etale de Pleine Mer

2,6 m.

4,2 m.

ISLE OF WIGHT

Approximate equivalents :

15 mins before
H.W. DOVER

5 hours after
H.W. ST MALO

4½ hours after
H.W. ST HELIER

30 mins before
H.W. PORTSMOUTH

1 hour after
H.W. LE HAVRE

0 1 2 3 4 5 6 7 8 9 10 Nautical miles
Mile marins

Convert Mean Rates shown on chartlets through table, opposite page

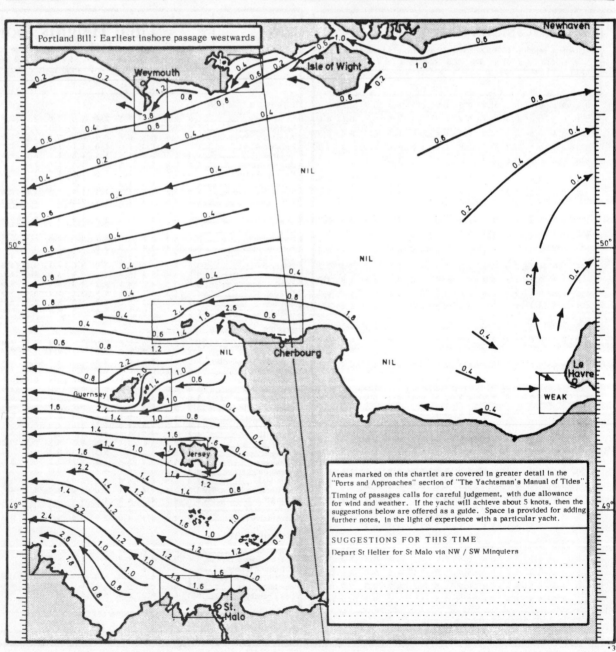

Portland Bill : Earliest inshore passage westwards

Weymouth

Isle of Wight

Newhaven

NIL

NIL

NIL

Cherbourg

NIL

Le Havre

WEAK

Guernsey

Jersey

St. Malo

Areas marked on this chartlet are covered in greater detail in the "Ports and Approaches" section of "The Yachtsman's Manual of Tides".

Timing of passages calls for careful judgement, with due allowance for wind and weather. If the yacht will achieve about 5 knots, then the suggestions below are offered as a guide. Space is provided for adding further notes, in the light of experience with a particular yacht.

SUGGESTIONS FOR THIS TIME
Depart St Helier for St Malo via NW / SW Minquiers

. . . .
. . . .
. . . .
. . . .
. . . .

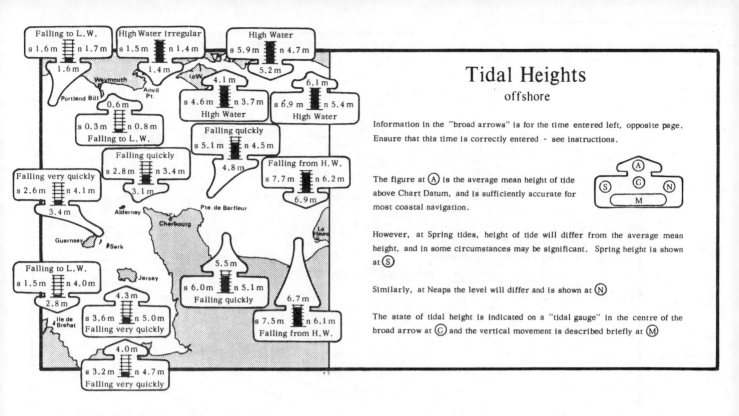

Tidal Heights
offshore

Information in the "broad arrows" is for the time entered left, opposite page. Ensure that this time is correctly entered - see instructions.

The figure at (A) is the average mean height of tide above Chart Datum, and is sufficiently accurate for most coastal navigation.

However, at Spring tides, height of tide will differ from the average mean height, and in some circumstances may be significant. Spring height is shown at (S)

Similarly, at Neaps the level will differ and is shown at (N)

The state of tidal height is indicated on a "tidal gauge" in the centre of the broad arrow at (G) and the vertical movement is described briefly at (M)

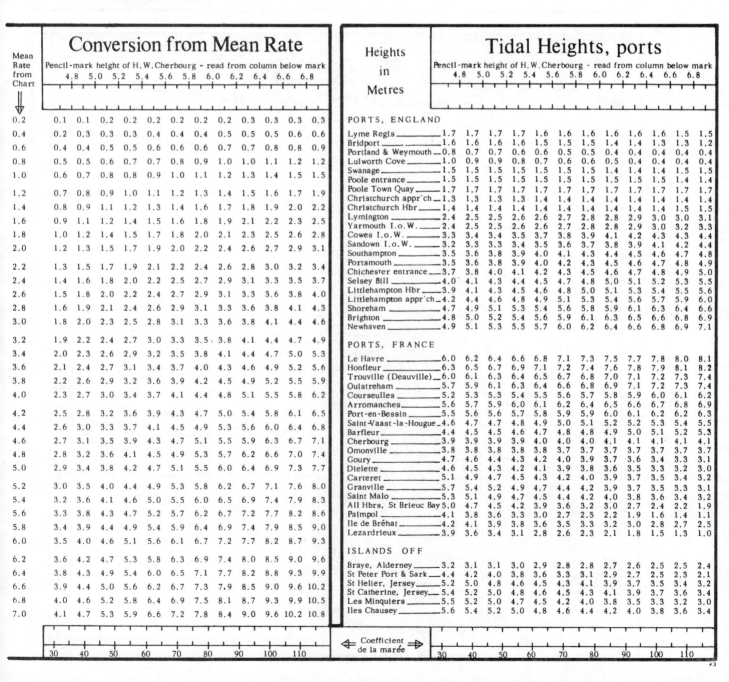

Conversion from Mean Rate

Pencil-mark height of H.W. Cherbourg - read from column below mark

Mean Rate from Chart		4.8	5.0	5.2	5.4	5.6	5.8	6.0	6.2	6.4	6.6	6.8
0.2	0.1	0.1	0.2	0.2	0.2	0.2	0.2	0.2	0.3	0.3	0.3	0.3
0.4	0.2	0.3	0.3	0.3	0.4	0.4	0.4	0.5	0.5	0.5	0.6	0.6
0.6	0.4	0.4	0.5	0.5	0.6	0.6	0.6	0.7	0.7	0.8	0.8	0.9
0.8	0.5	0.5	0.6	0.7	0.7	0.8	0.9	1.0	1.0	1.1	1.2	1.2
1.0	0.6	0.7	0.8	0.8	0.9	1.0	1.1	1.2	1.3	1.4	1.5	1.5
1.2	0.7	0.8	0.9	1.0	1.1	1.2	1.3	1.4	1.5	1.6	1.7	1.9
1.4	0.8	0.9	1.1	1.2	1.3	1.4	1.6	1.7	1.8	1.9	2.0	2.2
1.6	0.9	1.1	1.2	1.4	1.5	1.6	1.8	1.9	2.1	2.2	2.3	2.5
1.8	1.0	1.2	1.4	1.5	1.7	1.8	2.0	2.1	2.3	2.5	2.6	2.8
2.0	1.2	1.3	1.5	1.7	1.9	2.0	2.2	2.4	2.6	2.7	2.9	3.1
2.2	1.3	1.5	1.7	1.9	2.1	2.2	2.4	2.6	2.8	3.0	3.2	3.4
2.4	1.4	1.6	1.8	2.0	2.2	2.5	2.7	2.9	3.1	3.3	3.5	3.7
2.6	1.5	1.8	2.0	2.2	2.4	2.7	2.9	3.1	3.3	3.6	3.8	4.0
2.8	1.6	1.9	2.1	2.4	2.6	2.9	3.1	3.3	3.6	3.8	4.1	4.3
3.0	1.8	2.0	2.3	2.5	2.8	3.1	3.3	3.6	3.8	4.1	4.4	4.6
3.2	1.9	2.2	2.4	2.7	3.0	3.3	3.5	3.8	4.1	4.4	4.7	4.9
3.4	2.0	2.3	2.6	2.9	3.2	3.5	3.8	4.1	4.4	4.7	5.0	5.3
3.6	2.1	2.4	2.7	3.1	3.4	3.7	4.0	4.3	4.6	4.9	5.2	5.6
3.8	2.2	2.6	2.9	3.2	3.6	3.9	4.2	4.5	4.9	5.2	5.5	5.9
4.0	2.3	2.7	3.0	3.4	3.7	4.1	4.4	4.8	5.1	5.5	5.8	6.2
4.2	2.5	2.8	3.2	3.6	3.9	4.3	4.7	5.0	5.4	5.8	6.1	6.5
4.4	2.6	3.0	3.3	3.7	4.1	4.5	4.9	5.3	5.6	6.0	6.4	6.8
4.6	2.7	3.1	3.5	3.9	4.3	4.7	5.1	5.5	5.9	6.3	6.7	7.1
4.8	2.8	3.2	3.6	4.1	4.5	4.9	5.3	5.7	6.2	6.6	7.0	7.4
5.0	2.9	3.4	3.8	4.2	4.7	5.1	5.5	6.0	6.4	6.9	7.3	7.7
5.2	3.0	3.5	4.0	4.4	4.9	5.3	5.8	6.2	6.7	7.1	7.6	8.0
5.4	3.2	3.6	4.1	4.6	5.0	5.5	6.0	6.5	6.9	7.4	7.9	8.3
5.6	3.3	3.8	4.3	4.7	5.2	5.7	6.2	6.7	7.2	7.7	8.2	8.6
5.8	3.4	3.9	4.4	4.9	5.4	5.9	6.4	6.9	7.4	7.9	8.5	9.0
6.0	3.5	4.0	4.6	5.1	5.6	6.1	6.7	7.2	7.7	8.2	8.7	9.3
6.2	3.6	4.2	4.7	5.3	5.8	6.3	6.9	7.4	8.0	8.5	9.0	9.6
6.4	3.8	4.3	4.9	5.4	6.0	6.5	7.1	7.7	8.2	8.8	9.3	9.9
6.6	3.9	4.4	5.0	5.6	6.2	6.7	7.3	7.9	8.5	9.0	9.6	10.2
6.8	4.0	4.6	5.2	5.8	6.4	6.9	7.5	8.1	8.7	9.3	9.9	10.5
7.0	4.1	4.7	5.3	5.9	6.6	7.2	7.8	8.4	9.0	9.6	10.2	10.8

Tidal Heights, ports

Heights in Metres

Pencil-mark height of H.W. Cherbourg - read from column below mark

Port		4.8	5.0	5.2	5.4	5.6	5.8	6.0	6.2	6.4	6.6	6.8
PORTS, ENGLAND												
Lyme Regis	1.7	1.7	1.7	1.7	1.6	1.6	1.6	1.6	1.6	1.6	1.5	1.5
Bridport	1.6	1.6	1.6	1.6	1.5	1.5	1.5	1.4	1.4	1.3	1.3	1.2
Portland & Weymouth	0.8	0.7	0.7	0.6	0.6	0.5	0.5	0.4	0.4	0.4	0.4	0.4
Lulworth Cove	1.0	0.9	0.9	0.8	0.7	0.6	0.6	0.5	0.4	0.4	0.4	0.4
Swanage	1.5	1.5	1.5	1.5	1.5	1.5	1.5	1.4	1.4	1.4	1.5	1.5
Poole entrance	1.5	1.5	1.5	1.5	1.5	1.5	1.5	1.5	1.5	1.5	1.4	1.4
Poole Town Quay	1.7	1.7	1.7	1.7	1.7	1.7	1.7	1.7	1.7	1.7	1.7	1.7
Christchurch appr'ch	1.3	1.3	1.3	1.3	1.4	1.4	1.4	1.4	1.4	1.4	1.4	1.4
Christchurch Hbr	1.4	1.4	1.4	1.4	1.4	1.4	1.4	1.4	1.4	1.4	1.5	1.5
Lymington	2.4	2.5	2.5	2.6	2.6	2.7	2.8	2.9	3.0	3.0	3.1	
Yarmouth I.o.W.	2.4	2.5	2.5	2.6	2.6	2.7	2.8	2.8	2.9	3.0	3.2	3.3
Cowes I.o.W.	3.3	3.4	3.4	3.5	3.7	3.8	3.9	4.1	4.2	4.3	4.3	4.4
Sandown I.o.W.	3.2	3.3	3.3	3.4	3.5	3.6	3.7	3.8	3.9	4.1	4.2	4.4
Southampton	3.5	3.6	3.8	3.9	4.0	4.1	4.3	4.4	4.5	4.6	4.7	4.8
Portsmouth	3.5	3.6	3.8	3.9	4.0	4.2	4.3	4.5	4.6	4.7	4.8	4.9
Chichester entrance	3.7	3.8	4.0	4.1	4.2	4.3	4.5	4.6	4.7	4.8	4.9	5.0
Selsey Bill	4.0	4.1	4.3	4.4	4.5	4.7	4.8	5.0	5.1	5.2	5.3	5.5
Littlehampton Hbr	3.9	4.1	4.3	4.5	4.6	4.8	5.0	5.1	5.3	5.4	5.5	5.6
Littlehampton appr'ch	4.2	4.4	4.6	4.8	4.9	5.1	5.3	5.4	5.6	5.7	5.9	6.0
Shoreham	4.7	4.9	5.1	5.3	5.4	5.6	5.8	5.9	6.1	6.3	6.4	6.6
Brighton	4.8	5.0	5.2	5.4	5.6	5.9	6.1	6.3	6.5	6.6	6.8	6.9
Newhaven	4.9	5.1	5.3	5.5	5.7	6.0	6.2	6.4	6.6	6.8	6.9	7.1
PORTS, FRANCE												
Le Havre	6.0	6.2	6.4	6.6	6.8	7.1	7.3	7.5	7.7	7.8	8.0	8.1
Honfleur	6.3	6.5	6.7	6.9	7.1	7.2	7.4	7.6	7.8	7.9	8.1	8.2
Trouville (Deauville)	6.0	6.1	6.3	6.4	6.5	6.7	6.8	7.0	7.1	7.2	7.3	7.4
Ouistreham	5.7	5.9	6.1	6.3	6.4	6.6	6.8	6.9	7.1	7.2	7.3	7.4
Courseulles	5.2	5.3	5.3	5.4	5.5	5.6	5.7	5.8	5.9	6.0	6.1	6.2
Arromanches	5.6	5.7	5.9	6.0	6.1	6.2	6.4	6.5	6.6	6.7	6.8	6.9
Port-en-Bessin	5.5	5.6	5.6	5.7	5.8	5.9	5.9	6.0	6.1	6.2	6.2	6.3
Saint-Vaast-la-Hougue	4.6	4.7	4.7	4.8	4.9	5.0	5.1	5.2	5.2	5.3	5.4	5.5
Barfleur	4.4	4.5	4.5	4.6	4.7	4.8	4.8	4.9	5.0	5.1	5.2	5.3
Cherbourg	3.9	3.9	3.9	3.9	4.0	4.0	4.0	4.1	4.1	4.1	4.1	4.1
Omonville	3.8	3.8	3.8	3.8	3.8	3.7	3.7	3.7	3.7	3.7	3.7	3.7
Goury	4.7	4.6	4.4	4.3	4.2	4.0	3.9	3.7	3.6	3.4	3.3	3.1
Dielette	4.6	4.5	4.3	4.2	4.1	3.9	3.8	3.6	3.5	3.3	3.2	3.0
Carteret	5.1	4.9	4.7	4.5	4.3	4.2	4.0	3.9	3.7	3.5	3.4	3.2
Granville	5.7	5.4	5.2	4.9	4.7	4.4	4.2	3.9	3.7	3.5	3.3	3.1
Saint Malo	5.3	5.1	4.9	4.7	4.5	4.4	4.2	4.0	3.8	3.6	3.4	3.2
All Hbrs, St Brieuc Bay	5.0	4.7	4.5	4.2	3.9	3.6	3.2	3.0	2.7	2.4	2.2	1.9
Paimpol	4.1	3.8	3.6	3.3	3.0	2.7	2.5	2.2	1.9	1.6	1.4	1.1
Ile de Bréhat	4.2	4.1	3.9	3.8	3.6	3.5	3.3	3.2	3.0	2.8	2.7	2.5
Lezardrieux	3.9	3.6	3.4	3.1	2.8	2.6	2.3	2.1	1.8	1.5	1.3	1.0
ISLANDS OFF												
Braye, Alderney	3.2	3.1	3.1	3.0	2.9	2.8	2.8	2.7	2.6	2.5	2.5	2.4
St Peter Port & Sark	4.4	4.2	4.0	3.8	3.6	3.3	3.1	2.9	2.7	2.5	2.3	2.1
St Helier, Jersey	5.2	5.0	4.8	4.6	4.5	4.3	4.1	3.9	3.7	3.5	3.4	3.2
St Catherine, Jersey	5.4	5.2	5.0	4.8	4.6	4.5	4.3	4.1	3.9	3.7	3.6	3.4
Les Minquiers	5.5	5.2	5.0	4.7	4.5	4.2	4.0	3.8	3.5	3.3	3.2	3.0
Iles Chausey	5.6	5.4	5.2	5.0	4.8	4.6	4.4	4.2	4.0	3.8	3.6	3.4

⇐ Coefficient de la marée ⇒

30 40 50 60 70 80 90 100 110

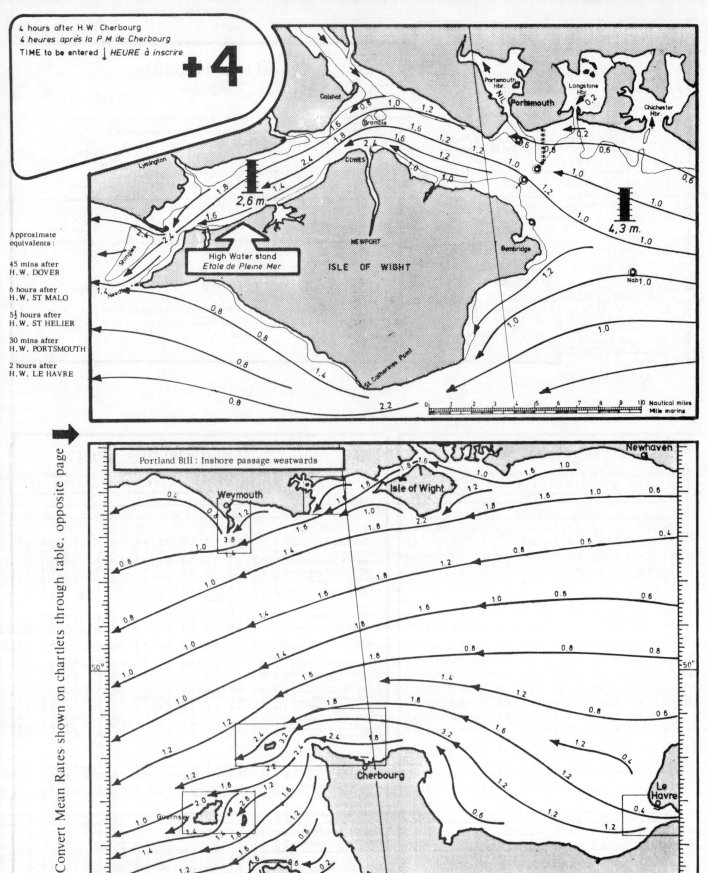

4 hours after H.W. Cherbourg
4 heures après la P.M. de Cherbourg
TIME to be entered ↓ HEURE à inscrire

+4

Approximate
equivalents :

45 mins after
H.W. DOVER

6 hours after
H.W. ST MALO

5½ hours after
H.W. ST HELIER

30 mins after
H.W. PORTSMOUTH

2 hours after
H.W. LE HAVRE

Calshot
Portsmouth Hbr.
NIL
Portsmouth
Langstone Hbr. 0.2
Chichester Hbr.
Bramble
COWES
Lymington
2,6 m.
High Water stand
Etale de Pleine Mer
Shingles
Needles
NEWPORT
ISLE OF WIGHT
Bembridge
Nab 1.0
4,3 m.
St. Catherine's Point

0 1 2 3 4 5 6 7 8 9 10 Nautical miles
Mile marins

Convert Mean Rates shown on chartlets through table, opposite page

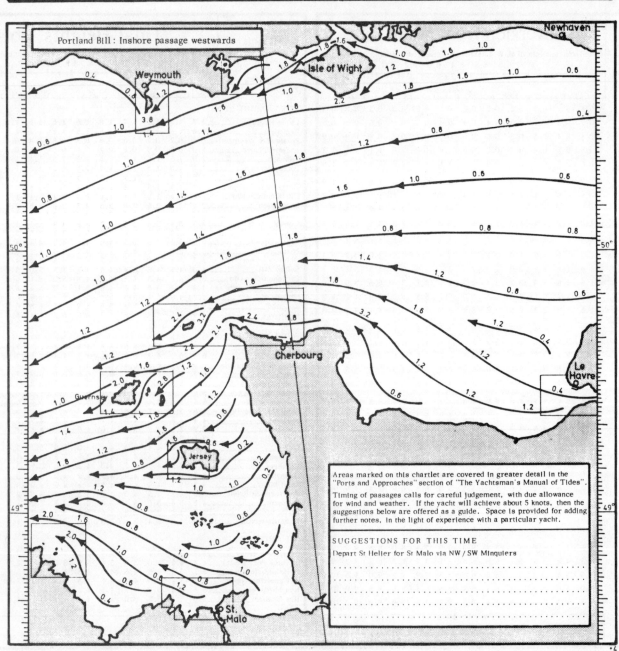

Portland Bill: Inshore passage westwards

Newhaven
Weymouth
3.8
Isle of Wight
Cherbourg
Le Havre
Guernsey
Jersey
50°
49°
St. Malo

Areas marked on this chartlet are covered in greater detail in the
"Ports and Approaches" section of "The Yachtsman's Manual of Tides".

Timing of passages calls for careful judgement, with due allowance
for wind and weather. If the yacht will achieve about 5 knots, then the
suggestions below are offered as a guide. Space is provided for adding
further notes, in the light of experience with a particular yacht.

SUGGESTIONS FOR THIS TIME
Depart St Helier for St Malo via NW / SW Minquiers
. . . .
. . . .
. . . .
. . . .
. . . .

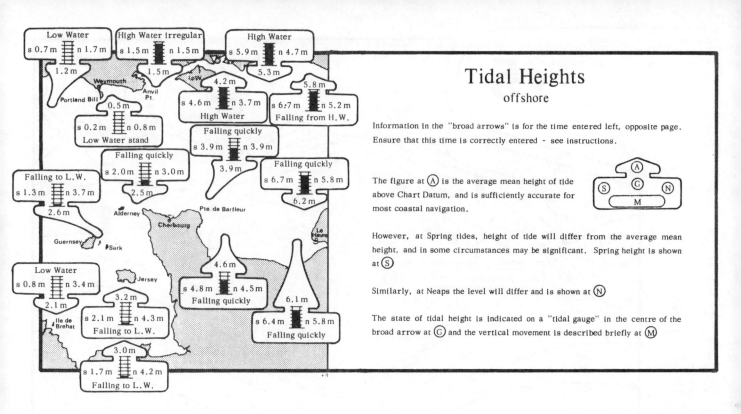

Tidal Heights
offshore

Information in the "broad arrows" is for the time entered left, opposite page. Ensure that this time is correctly entered - see instructions.

The figure at (A) is the average mean height of tide above Chart Datum, and is sufficiently accurate for most coastal navigation.

However, at Spring tides, height of tide will differ from the average mean height, and in some circumstances may be significant. Spring height is shown at (S)

Similarly, at Neaps the level will differ and is shown at (N)

The state of tidal height is indicated on a "tidal gauge" in the centre of the broad arrow at (G) and the vertical movement is described briefly at (M)

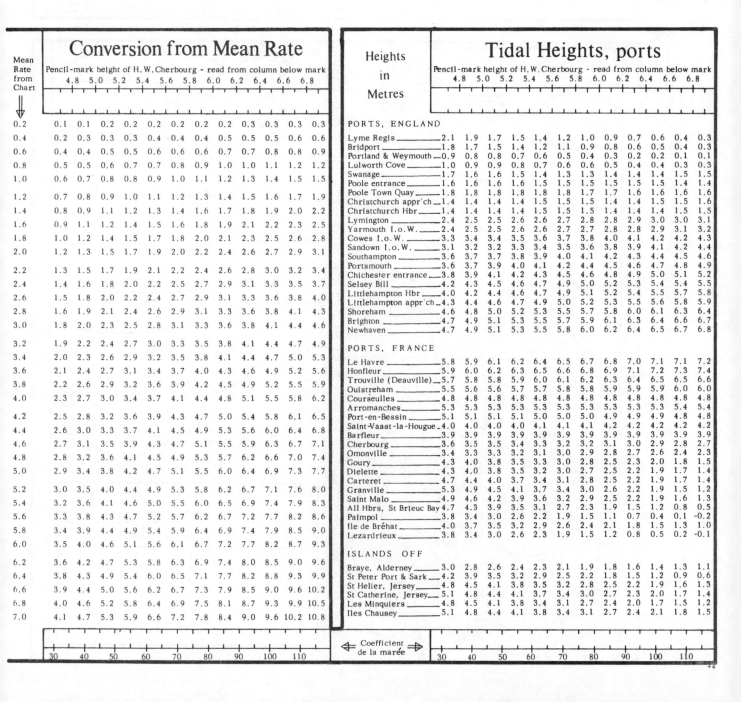

Conversion from Mean Rate

Pencil-mark height of H.W. Cherbourg - read from column below mark

Mean Rate from Chart		4.8	5.0	5.2	5.4	5.6	5.8	6.0	6.2	6.4	6.6	6.8
0.2	0.1	0.1	0.2	0.2	0.2	0.2	0.2	0.2	0.3	0.3	0.3	0.3
0.4	0.2	0.3	0.3	0.3	0.4	0.4	0.4	0.5	0.5	0.5	0.6	0.6
0.6	0.4	0.4	0.5	0.5	0.6	0.6	0.6	0.7	0.7	0.8	0.8	0.9
0.8	0.5	0.5	0.6	0.7	0.7	0.8	0.9	1.0	1.0	1.1	1.2	1.2
1.0	0.6	0.7	0.8	0.8	0.9	1.0	1.1	1.2	1.3	1.4	1.5	1.5
1.2	0.7	0.8	0.9	1.0	1.1	1.2	1.3	1.4	1.5	1.6	1.7	1.9
1.4	0.8	0.9	1.1	1.2	1.3	1.4	1.6	1.7	1.8	1.9	2.0	2.2
1.6	0.9	1.1	1.2	1.4	1.5	1.6	1.8	1.9	2.1	2.2	2.3	2.5
1.8	1.0	1.2	1.4	1.5	1.7	1.8	2.0	2.1	2.3	2.5	2.6	2.8
2.0	1.2	1.3	1.5	1.7	1.9	2.0	2.2	2.4	2.6	2.7	2.9	3.1
2.2	1.3	1.5	1.7	1.9	2.1	2.2	2.4	2.6	2.8	3.0	3.2	3.4
2.4	1.4	1.6	1.8	2.0	2.2	2.5	2.7	2.9	3.1	3.3	3.5	3.7
2.6	1.5	1.8	2.0	2.2	2.4	2.7	2.9	3.1	3.3	3.6	3.8	4.0
2.8	1.6	1.9	2.1	2.4	2.6	2.9	3.1	3.3	3.6	3.8	4.1	4.3
3.0	1.8	2.0	2.3	2.5	2.8	3.1	3.3	3.6	3.8	4.1	4.4	4.6
3.2	1.9	2.2	2.4	2.7	3.0	3.3	3.5	3.8	4.1	4.4	4.7	4.9
3.4	2.0	2.3	2.6	2.9	3.2	3.5	3.8	4.1	4.4	4.7	5.0	5.3
3.6	2.1	2.4	2.7	3.1	3.4	3.7	4.0	4.3	4.6	4.9	5.2	5.6
3.8	2.2	2.6	2.9	3.2	3.6	3.9	4.2	4.5	4.9	5.2	5.5	5.9
4.0	2.3	2.7	3.0	3.4	3.7	4.1	4.4	4.8	5.1	5.5	5.8	6.2
4.2	2.5	2.8	3.2	3.6	3.9	4.3	4.7	5.0	5.4	5.8	6.1	6.5
4.4	2.6	3.0	3.3	3.7	4.1	4.5	4.9	5.3	5.6	6.0	6.4	6.8
4.6	2.7	3.1	3.5	3.9	4.3	4.7	5.1	5.5	5.9	6.3	6.7	7.1
4.8	2.8	3.2	3.6	4.1	4.5	4.9	5.3	5.7	6.2	6.6	7.0	7.4
5.0	2.9	3.4	3.8	4.2	4.7	5.1	5.5	6.0	6.4	6.9	7.3	7.7
5.2	3.0	3.5	4.0	4.4	4.9	5.3	5.8	6.2	6.7	7.1	7.6	8.0
5.4	3.2	3.6	4.1	4.6	5.0	5.5	6.0	6.5	6.9	7.4	7.9	8.3
5.6	3.3	3.8	4.3	4.7	5.2	5.7	6.2	6.7	7.2	7.7	8.2	8.6
5.8	3.4	3.9	4.4	4.9	5.4	5.9	6.4	6.9	7.4	7.9	8.5	9.0
6.0	3.5	4.0	4.6	5.1	5.6	6.1	6.7	7.2	7.7	8.2	8.7	9.3
6.2	3.6	4.2	4.7	5.3	5.8	6.3	6.9	7.4	8.0	8.5	9.0	9.6
6.4	3.8	4.3	4.9	5.4	6.0	6.5	7.1	7.7	8.2	8.8	9.3	9.9
6.6	3.9	4.4	5.0	5.6	6.2	6.7	7.3	7.9	8.5	9.0	9.6	10.2
6.8	4.0	4.6	5.2	5.8	6.4	6.9	7.5	8.1	8.7	9.3	9.9	10.5
7.0	4.1	4.7	5.3	5.9	6.6	7.2	7.8	8.4	9.0	9.6	10.2	10.8

Tidal Heights, ports

Heights in Metres

Pencil-mark height of H.W. Cherbourg - read from column below mark

Port		4.8	5.0	5.2	5.4	5.6	5.8	6.0	6.2	6.4	6.6	6.8
PORTS, ENGLAND												
Lyme Regis	2.1	1.9	1.7	1.5	1.4	1.2	1.0	0.9	0.7	0.6	0.4	0.3
Bridport	1.8	1.7	1.5	1.4	1.2	1.1	0.9	0.8	0.6	0.5	0.4	0.3
Portland & Weymouth	0.9	0.8	0.8	0.7	0.6	0.5	0.4	0.3	0.2	0.2	0.1	0.1
Lulworth Cove	1.0	0.9	0.9	0.8	0.7	0.6	0.6	0.5	0.4	0.4	0.3	0.3
Swanage	1.7	1.6	1.6	1.5	1.4	1.3	1.3	1.4	1.4	1.4	1.5	1.5
Poole entrance	1.6	1.6	1.6	1.6	1.5	1.5	1.5	1.5	1.5	1.5	1.4	1.4
Poole Town Quay	1.8	1.8	1.8	1.8	1.8	1.8	1.7	1.7	1.6	1.6	1.6	1.6
Christchurch appr'ch	1.4	1.4	1.4	1.4	1.5	1.5	1.5	1.4	1.4	1.5	1.5	1.6
Christchurch Hbr	1.4	1.4	1.4	1.4	1.5	1.5	1.5	1.4	1.4	1.4	1.5	1.5
Lymington	2.4	2.5	2.5	2.6	2.6	2.7	2.8	2.9	3.0	3.0	3.1	
Yarmouth I.o.W.	2.4	2.5	2.5	2.6	2.6	2.7	2.7	2.8	2.8	2.9	3.1	3.2
Cowes I.o.W.	3.3	3.4	3.4	3.5	3.6	3.7	3.8	4.0	4.1	4.2	4.2	4.3
Sandown I.o.W.	3.1	3.2	3.2	3.3	3.4	3.5	3.6	3.8	3.9	4.1	4.2	4.4
Southampton	3.6	3.7	3.7	3.8	3.9	4.0	4.1	4.2	4.3	4.4	4.5	4.6
Portsmouth	3.6	3.7	3.9	4.0	4.1	4.2	4.4	4.5	4.6	4.7	4.8	4.9
Chichester entrance	3.8	3.9	4.1	4.2	4.3	4.5	4.6	4.8	4.9	5.0	5.1	5.2
Selsey Bill	4.2	4.3	4.5	4.6	4.7	4.9	5.0	5.2	5.3	5.4	5.4	5.5
Littlehampton Hbr	4.0	4.2	4.4	4.6	4.7	4.9	5.1	5.2	5.4	5.5	5.7	5.8
Littlehampton appr'ch	4.3	4.4	4.6	4.7	4.9	5.0	5.2	5.3	5.5	5.6	5.8	5.9
Shoreham	4.6	4.8	5.0	5.2	5.3	5.5	5.7	5.8	6.0	6.1	6.3	6.4
Brighton	4.7	4.9	5.1	5.3	5.5	5.7	5.9	6.1	6.3	6.4	6.6	6.7
Newhaven	4.7	4.9	5.1	5.3	5.5	5.8	6.0	6.2	6.4	6.5	6.7	6.8
PORTS, FRANCE												
Le Havre	5.8	5.9	6.1	6.2	6.4	6.5	6.7	6.8	7.0	7.1	7.1	7.2
Honfleur	5.9	6.0	6.2	6.3	6.5	6.6	6.8	6.9	7.1	7.2	7.3	7.4
Trouville (Deauville)	5.7	5.8	5.8	5.9	6.0	6.1	6.2	6.3	6.4	6.5	6.5	6.6
Ouistreham	5.5	5.6	5.6	5.7	5.7	5.8	5.8	5.9	5.9	5.9	6.0	6.0
Courseulles	4.8	4.8	4.8	4.8	4.8	4.8	4.8	4.8	4.8	4.8	4.8	4.8
Arromanches	5.3	5.3	5.3	5.3	5.3	5.3	5.3	5.3	5.3	5.3	5.4	5.4
Port-en-Bessin	5.1	5.1	5.1	5.1	5.0	5.0	5.0	4.9	4.9	4.9	4.8	4.8
Saint-Vaast-la-Hougue	4.0	4.0	4.0	4.0	4.1	4.1	4.1	4.2	4.2	4.2	4.2	4.2
Barfleur	3.9	3.9	3.9	3.9	3.9	3.9	3.9	3.9	3.9	3.9	3.9	3.9
Cherbourg	3.6	3.5	3.5	3.4	3.3	3.2	3.2	3.1	3.0	2.9	2.8	2.7
Omonville	3.4	3.3	3.3	3.2	3.1	3.0	2.9	2.8	2.7	2.6	2.4	2.3
Goury	4.3	4.0	3.8	3.5	3.3	3.0	2.8	2.5	2.3	2.0	1.8	1.5
Dielette	4.3	4.0	3.8	3.5	3.2	3.0	2.7	2.5	2.2	1.9	1.7	1.4
Carteret	4.7	4.4	4.0	3.7	3.4	3.1	2.8	2.5	2.2	1.9	1.7	1.4
Granville	5.3	4.9	4.5	4.1	3.7	3.4	3.0	2.6	2.2	1.9	1.5	1.2
Saint Malo	4.9	4.6	4.2	3.9	3.6	3.2	2.9	2.5	2.2	1.9	1.6	1.3
All Hbrs, St Brieuc Bay	4.7	4.3	3.9	3.5	3.1	2.7	2.3	1.9	1.5	1.2	0.8	0.5
Paimpol	3.8	3.4	3.0	2.6	2.2	1.9	1.5	1.1	0.7	0.4	0.1	-0.2
Ile de Bréhat	4.0	3.7	3.5	3.2	2.9	2.6	2.4	2.1	1.8	1.5	1.3	1.0
Lezardrieux	3.8	3.4	3.0	2.6	2.3	1.9	1.5	1.2	0.8	0.5	0.2	-0.1
ISLANDS OFF												
Braye, Alderney	3.0	2.8	2.6	2.4	2.3	2.1	1.9	1.8	1.6	1.4	1.3	1.1
St Peter Port & Sark	4.2	3.9	3.5	3.2	2.9	2.5	2.2	1.8	1.5	1.2	0.9	0.6
St Helier, Jersey	4.8	4.5	4.1	3.8	3.5	3.2	2.8	2.5	2.2	1.9	1.6	1.3
St Catherine, Jersey	5.1	4.8	4.4	4.1	3.7	3.4	3.0	2.7	2.3	2.0	1.7	1.4
Les Minquiers	4.8	4.5	4.1	3.8	3.4	3.1	2.7	2.4	2.0	1.7	1.5	1.2
Iles Chausey	5.1	4.8	4.4	4.1	3.8	3.4	3.1	2.7	2.4	2.1	1.8	1.5

⇐ Coefficient de la marée ⇒

30 40 50 60 70 80 90 100 110

5 hours after H.W. Cherbourg
5 heures après la P.M. de Cherbourg
TIME to be entered ↓ *HEURE à inscrire*

+5

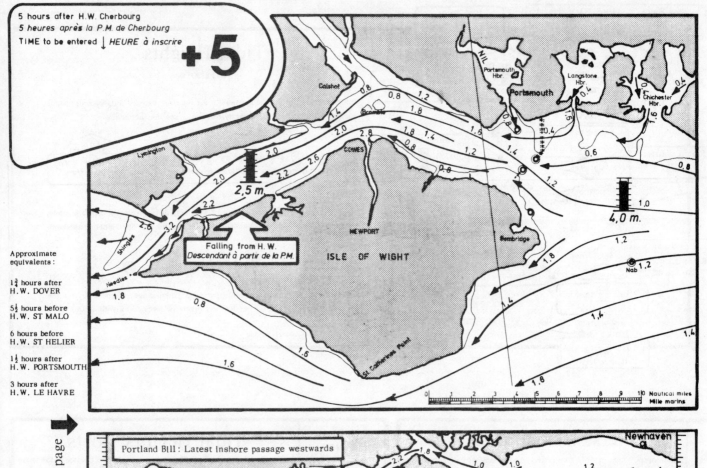

Calshot 0.8 0.8 1.2
Bramble 1.8
2.0
2.0 2.8 1.8 1.4
COWES 2.6 0.8
2.2 2.2
2,5 m
2.0
2.2
2.6 3.2
Shingles
Lymington
Needles 1.8
0.8
1.6
1.6
1.8
St. Catharines Point

Portsmouth Hbr.
Portsmouth
Langstone Hbr. 0.4
NIL Chichester Hbr. 0.4 0.4
0.8 1.6 0.4
1.6 1.2 1.4
0.8 1.2 0.6 0.8
0.8 1.2
4,0 m. 1.0
Bembridge 1.2
1.8 Nab 1.2
1.4 1.2
1.4
1.4

Falling from H.W.
Descendant à partir de la P.M.

ISLE OF WIGHT

NEWPORT

0 1 2 3 4 5 6 7 8 9 10 Nautical miles
Mille marins

Approximate
equivalents :

1¾ hours after
H.W. DOVER

5½ hours before
H.W. ST MALO

6 hours before
H.W. ST HELIER

1½ hours after
H.W. PORTSMOUTH

3 hours after
H.W. LE HAVRE

Convert Mean Rates shown on chartlets through table, opposite page

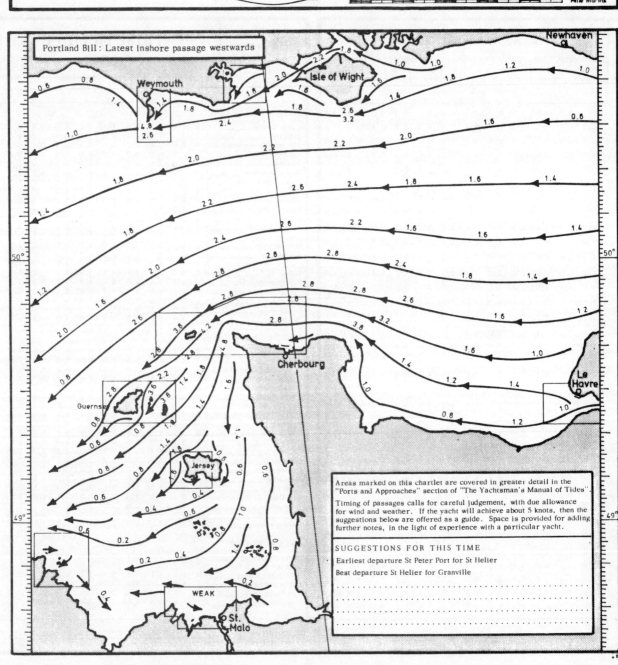

Portland Bill : Latest inshore passage westwards

Newhaven
1.8 2.2 1.8
0.8 2.0 Isle of Wight 1.0 1.0 1.8 1.2
0.6 0.8 **Weymouth** 1.8 1.8 1.6 1.0
1.4 1.4 1.8 2.6 1.4
1.0 4.8 2.4 3.2 0.8
2.6 2.0
2.2 2.2
2.0
1.8 2.6 2.4 1.8 1.6 1.4
2.2 1.4
1.8 2.6 1.6 1.6
2.4 2.0
50° 2.8 2.8 1.8 1.4 **50°**
2.0 2.8 2.4
1.6 2.8 2.6
1.2 2.6 2.8 1.6
2.0 3.8 4.2 2.8 3.2 1.0
2.8 4.8 3.8 1.2
0.8 2.8 **Cherbourg** 1.4
2.8 3.6 2.2 1.4 1.8 1.6 1.2 1.4 **Le Havre**
Guernsey 3.8 1.8 0.8 1.0
0.8 1.4 0.8 1.2
0.6 1.8 **Jersey** 0.6 1.0
0.8 0.5 0.4 0.6 0.6
0.6 0.4 1.0
49° 0.6 0.2 0.8 **49°**
0.2 0.4 0.8
0.5 0.4 1.6
0.2 0.2
WEAK
0.5 **St. Malo**

Areas marked on this chartlet are covered in greater detail in the
"Ports and Approaches" section of "The Yachtsman's Manual of Tides".

Timing of passages calls for careful judgement, with due allowance
for wind and weather. If the yacht will achieve about 5 knots, then the
suggestions below are offered as a guide. Space is provided for adding
further notes, in the light of experience with a particular yacht.

SUGGESTIONS FOR THIS TIME

Earliest departure St Peter Port for St Helier

Best departure St Helier for Granville

· ·

· ·

· ·

· ·

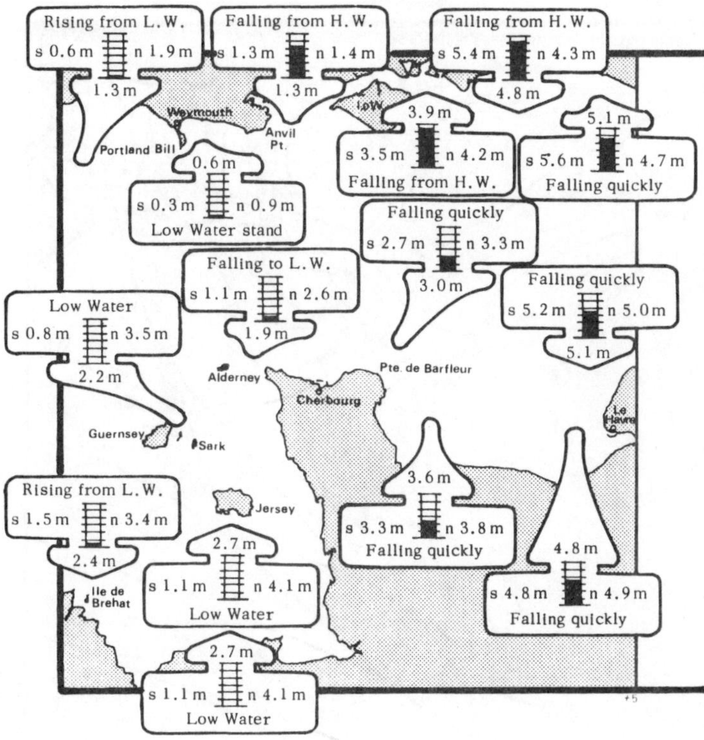

Rising from L.W.
s 0.6 m n 1.9 m
1.3 m
Falling from H.W.
s 1.3 m n 1.4 m
1.3 m
Falling from H.W.
s 5.4 m n 4.3 m
4.8 m
Weymouth
Portland Bill
Anvil Pt.
IoW
3.9 m
s 3.5 m n 4.2 m
Falling from H.W.
5.1 m
s 5.6 m n 4.7 m
Falling quickly
0.6 m
s 0.3 m n 0.9 m
Low Water stand
Falling quickly
s 2.7 m n 3.3 m
3.0 m
Falling to L.W.
s 1.1 m n 2.6 m
1.9 m
Falling quickly
s 5.2 m n 5.0 m
5.1 m
Low Water
s 0.8 m n 3.5 m
2.2 m
Alderney
Pte. de Barfleur
Cherbourg
Le Havre
Guernsey
Sark
3.6 m
s 3.3 m n 3.8 m
Falling quickly
4.8 m
s 4.8 m n 4.9 m
Falling quickly
Rising from L.W.
s 1.5 m n 3.4 m
2.4 m
Jersey
2.7 m
s 1.1 m n 4.1 m
Low Water
Ile de Brehat
2.7 m
s 1.1 m n 4.1 m
Low Water

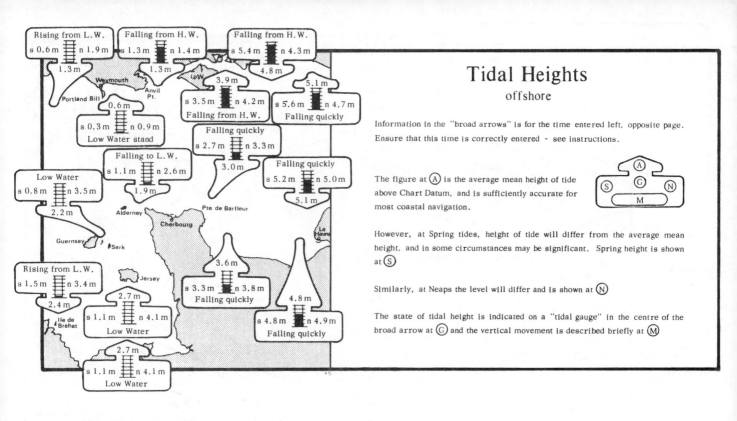

Tidal Heights

offshore

Information in the "broad arrows" is for the time entered left, opposite page. Ensure that this time is correctly entered - see instructions.

The figure at (A) is the average mean height of tide above Chart Datum, and is sufficiently accurate for most coastal navigation.

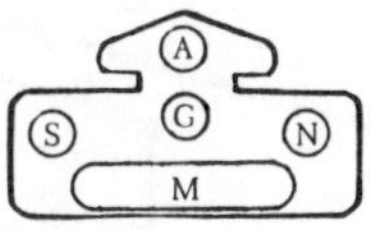

A
S
G
N
M

However, at Spring tides, height of tide will differ from the average mean height, and in some circumstances may be significant. Spring height is shown at (S)

Similarly, at Neaps the level will differ and is shown at (N)

The state of tidal height is indicated on a "tidal gauge" in the centre of the broad arrow at (G) and the vertical movement is described briefly at (M)

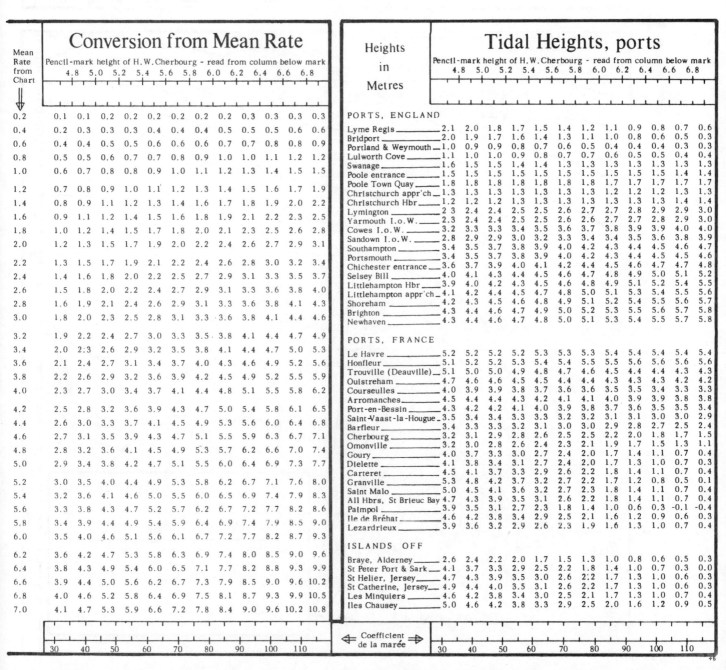

Conversion from Mean Rate

Pencil-mark height of H.W. Cherbourg - read from column below mark
4.8 5.0 5.2 5.4 5.6 5.8 6.0 6.2 6.4 6.6 6.8

Mean Rate from Chart ⇩												
0.2	0.1	0.1	0.2	0.2	0.2	0.2	0.2	0.2	0.3	0.3	0.3	0.3
0.4	0.2	0.3	0.3	0.3	0.4	0.4	0.4	0.5	0.5	0.5	0.6	0.6
0.6	0.4	0.4	0.5	0.5	0.6	0.6	0.6	0.7	0.7	0.8	0.8	0.9
0.8	0.5	0.5	0.6	0.7	0.7	0.8	0.9	1.0	1.0	1.1	1.2	1.2
1.0	0.6	0.7	0.8	0.8	0.9	1.0	1.1	1.2	1.3	1.4	1.5	1.5
1.2	0.7	0.8	0.9	1.0	1.1	1.2	1.3	1.4	1.5	1.6	1.7	1.9
1.4	0.8	0.9	1.1	1.2	1.3	1.4	1.6	1.7	1.8	1.9	2.0	2.2
1.6	0.9	1.1	1.2	1.4	1.5	1.6	1.8	1.9	2.1	2.2	2.3	2.5
1.8	1.0	1.2	1.4	1.5	1.7	1.8	2.0	2.1	2.3	2.5	2.6	2.8
2.0	1.2	1.3	1.5	1.7	1.9	2.0	2.2	2.4	2.6	2.7	2.9	3.1
2.2	1.3	1.5	1.7	1.9	2.1	2.2	2.4	2.6	2.8	3.0	3.2	3.4
2.4	1.4	1.6	1.8	2.0	2.2	2.5	2.7	2.9	3.1	3.3	3.5	3.7
2.6	1.5	1.8	2.0	2.2	2.4	2.7	2.9	3.1	3.3	3.6	3.8	4.0
2.8	1.6	1.9	2.1	2.4	2.6	2.9	3.1	3.3	3.6	3.8	4.1	4.3
3.0	1.8	2.0	2.3	2.5	2.8	3.1	3.3	3.6	3.8	4.1	4.4	4.6
3.2	1.9	2.2	2.4	2.7	3.0	3.3	3.5	3.8	4.1	4.4	4.7	4.9
3.4	2.0	2.3	2.6	2.9	3.2	3.5	3.8	4.1	4.4	4.7	5.0	5.3
3.6	2.1	2.4	2.7	3.1	3.4	3.7	4.0	4.3	4.6	4.9	5.2	5.6
3.8	2.2	2.6	2.9	3.2	3.6	3.9	4.2	4.5	4.9	5.2	5.5	5.9
4.0	2.3	2.7	3.0	3.4	3.7	4.1	4.4	4.8	5.1	5.5	5.8	6.2
4.2	2.5	2.8	3.2	3.6	3.9	4.3	4.7	5.0	5.4	5.8	6.1	6.5
4.4	2.6	3.0	3.3	3.7	4.1	4.5	4.9	5.3	5.6	6.0	6.4	6.8
4.6	2.7	3.1	3.5	3.9	4.3	4.7	5.1	5.5	5.9	6.3	6.7	7.1
4.8	2.8	3.2	3.6	4.1	4.5	4.9	5.3	5.7	6.2	6.6	7.0	7.4
5.0	2.9	3.4	3.8	4.2	4.7	5.1	5.5	6.0	6.4	6.9	7.3	7.7
5.2	3.0	3.5	4.0	4.4	4.9	5.3	5.8	6.2	6.7	7.1	7.6	8.0
5.4	3.2	3.6	4.1	4.6	5.0	5.5	6.0	6.5	6.9	7.4	7.9	8.3
5.6	3.3	3.8	4.3	4.7	5.2	5.7	6.2	6.7	7.2	7.7	8.2	8.6
5.8	3.4	3.9	4.4	4.9	5.4	5.9	6.4	6.9	7.4	7.9	8.5	9.0
6.0	3.5	4.0	4.6	5.1	5.6	6.1	6.7	7.2	7.7	8.2	8.7	9.3
6.2	3.6	4.2	4.7	5.3	5.8	6.3	6.9	7.4	8.0	8.5	9.0	9.6
6.4	3.8	4.3	4.9	5.4	6.0	6.5	7.1	7.7	8.2	8.8	9.3	9.9
6.6	3.9	4.4	5.0	5.6	6.2	6.7	7.3	7.9	8.5	9.0	9.6	10.2
6.8	4.0	4.6	5.2	5.8	6.4	6.9	7.5	8.1	8.7	9.3	9.9	10.5
7.0	4.1	4.7	5.3	5.9	6.6	7.2	7.8	8.4	9.0	9.6	10.2	10.8

30 40 50 60 70 80 90 100 110

⇦ Coefficient de la marée ⇨

30 40 50 60 70 80 90 100 110

Tidal Heights, ports

Heights in Metres

Pencil-mark height of H.W. Cherbourg - read from column below mark
4.8 5.0 5.2 5.4 5.6 5.8 6.0 6.2 6.4 6.6 6.8

PORTS, ENGLAND												
Lyme Regis	2.1	2.0	1.8	1.7	1.5	1.4	1.2	1.1	0.9	0.8	0.7	0.6
Bridport	2.0	1.9	1.7	1.6	1.4	1.3	1.1	1.0	0.8	0.6	0.5	0.3
Portland & Weymouth	1.0	0.9	0.9	0.8	0.7	0.6	0.5	0.4	0.4	0.4	0.3	0.3
Lulworth Cove	1.1	1.0	1.0	0.9	0.8	0.7	0.7	0.6	0.5	0.5	0.4	0.4
Swanage	1.6	1.5	1.5	1.4	1.4	1.3	1.3	1.3	1.3	1.3	1.3	1.3
Poole entrance	1.5	1.5	1.5	1.5	1.5	1.5	1.5	1.5	1.5	1.5	1.4	1.4
Poole Town Quay	1.8	1.8	1.8	1.8	1.8	1.8	1.8	1.7	1.7	1.7	1.7	1.7
Christchurch appr'ch	1.3	1.3	1.3	1.3	1.3	1.3	1.3	1.2	1.2	1.2	1.3	1.3
Christchurch Hbr	1.2	1.2	1.2	1.3	1.3	1.3	1.3	1.3	1.3	1.3	1.4	1.4
Lymington	2 3	2.4	2.4	2.5	2.5	2.6	2.7	2.7	2.8	2.9	2.9	3.0
Yarmouth I.o.W.	2.3	2.4	2.4	2.5	2.5	2.6	2.6	2.7	2.7	2.8	2.9	3.0
Cowes I.o.W.	3.2	3.3	3.3	3.4	3.5	3.6	3.7	3.8	3.9	3.9	4.0	4.0
Sandown I.o.W.	2.8	2.9	2.9	3.0	3.2	3.3	3.4	3.4	3.5	3.6	3.8	3.9
Southampton	3.4	3.5	3.7	3.8	3.9	4.0	4.2	4.3	4.4	4.5	4.6	4.7
Portsmouth	3.4	3.5	3.7	3.8	3.9	4.0	4.2	4.3	4.4	4.5	4.5	4.6
Chichester entrance	3.6	3.7	3.9	4.0	4.1	4.2	4.4	4.5	4.6	4.7	4.7	4.8
Selsey Bill	4.0	4.1	4.3	4.4	4.5	4.6	4.7	4.8	4.9	5.0	5.1	5.2
Littlehampton Hbr	3.9	4.0	4.2	4.3	4.5	4.6	4.8	4.9	5.1	5.2	5.4	5.5
Littlehampton appr'ch	4.1	4.2	4.4	4.5	4.7	4.8	5.0	5.1	5.3	5.4	5.5	5.6
Shoreham	4.2	4.3	4.5	4.6	4.8	4.9	5.1	5.2	5.4	5.5	5.6	5.7
Brighton	4.3	4.4	4.6	4.7	4.9	5.0	5.2	5.3	5.5	5.6	5.7	5.8
Newhaven	4.3	4.4	4.6	4.7	4.8	5.0	5.1	5.3	5.4	5.5	5.7	5.8
PORTS, FRANCE												
Le Havre	5.2	5.2	5.2	5.2	5.3	5.3	5.3	5.4	5.4	5.4	5.4	5.4
Honfleur	5.1	5.2	5.2	5.3	5.4	5.4	5.5	5.5	5.6	5.6	5.6	5.6
Trouville (Deauville)	5.1	5.0	5.0	4.9	4.8	4.7	4.6	4.5	4.4	4.4	4.3	4.3
Ouistreham	4.7	4.6	4.6	4.5	4.5	4.4	4.4	4.3	4.3	4.3	4.2	4.2
Courseulles	4.0	3.9	3.9	3.8	3.7	3.6	3.6	3.5	3.5	3.4	3.3	3.3
Arromanches	4.5	4.4	4.4	4.3	4.2	4.1	4.1	4.0	3.9	3.9	3.8	3.8
Port-en-Bessin	4.3	4.2	4.2	4.1	4.0	3.9	3.8	3.7	3.6	3.5	3.5	3.4
Saint-Vaast-la-Hougue	3.5	3.4	3.4	3.3	3.3	3.2	3.2	3.1	3.1	3.0	3.0	2.9
Barfleur	3.4	3.3	3.3	3.2	3.1	3.0	3.0	2.9	2.8	2.7	2.5	2.4
Cherbourg	3.2	3.1	2.9	2.8	2.6	2.5	2.5	2.2	2.0	1.8	1.7	1.5
Omonville	3.2	3.0	2.8	2.6	2.4	2.3	2.1	1.9	1.7	1.5	1.3	1.1
Goury	4.0	3.7	3.3	3.0	2.7	2.4	2.0	1.7	1.4	1.1	0.7	0.4
Dielette	4.1	3.8	3.4	3.1	2.7	2.4	2.0	1.7	1.3	1.0	0.7	0.3
Carteret	4.5	4.1	3.7	3.3	2.9	2.6	2.2	1.8	1.4	1.1	0.7	0.4
Granville	5.3	4.8	4.2	3.7	3.2	2.7	2.2	1.7	1.2	0.8	0.5	0.1
Saint Malo	5.0	4.5	4.1	3.6	3.2	2.7	2.3	1.8	1.4	1.1	0.7	0.4
All Hbrs, St Brieuc Bay	4.7	4.3	3.9	3.5	3.1	2.6	2.2	1.8	1.4	1.1	0.7	0.4
Paimpol	3.9	3.5	3.1	2.7	2.3	1.8	1.4	1.0	0.6	0.3	-0.1	-0.4
Ile de Bréhat	4.6	4.2	3.8	3.4	2.9	2.5	2.1	1.6	1.2	0.9	0.6	0.3
Lezardrieux	3.9	3.6	3.2	2.9	2.6	2.3	1.9	1.6	1.3	1.0	0.7	0.4
ISLANDS OFF												
Braye, Alderney	2.6	2.4	2.2	2.0	1.7	1.5	1.3	1.0	0.8	0.6	0.5	0.3
St Peter Port & Sark	4.1	3.7	3.3	2.9	2.5	2.2	1.8	1.4	1.0	0.7	0.3	0.0
St Helier, Jersey	4.7	4.3	3.9	3.5	3.0	2.6	2.2	1.7	1.3	1.0	0.6	0.3
St Catherine, Jersey	4.9	4.4	4.0	3.5	3.1	2.6	2.2	1.7	1.3	1.0	0.6	0.3
Les Minquiers	4.6	4.2	3.8	3.4	3.0	2.5	2.1	1.7	1.3	1.0	0.7	0.4
Iles Chausey	5.0	4.6	4.2	3.8	3.3	2.9	2.5	2.0	1.6	1.2	0.9	0.5

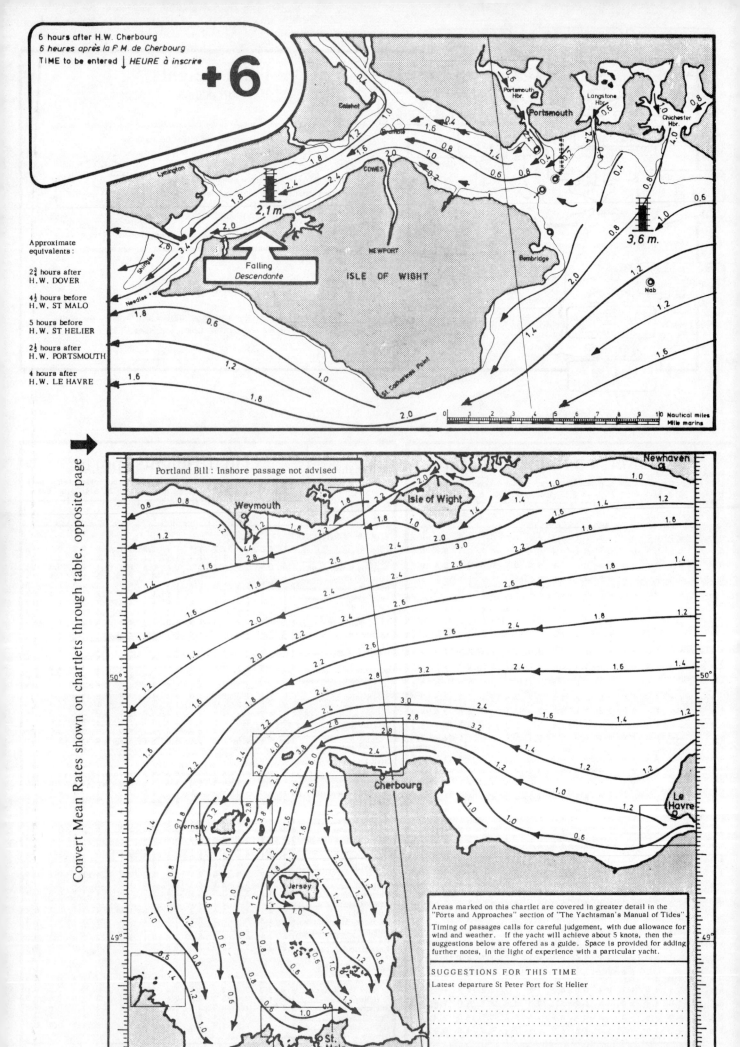

6 hours after H.W. Cherbourg
6 heures après la P.M. de Cherbourg
TIME to be entered ↓ *HEURE à inscrire*

+6

Approximate equivalents:

2¾ hours after H.W. DOVER

4½ hours before H.W. ST MALO

5 hours before H.W. ST HELIER

2½ hours after H.W. PORTSMOUTH

4 hours after H.W. LE HAVRE

Convert Mean Rates shown on chartlets through table, opposite page

Falling
Descendante

ISLE OF WIGHT

2,1 m.

3,6 m.

Portland Bill : Inshore passage not advised

Areas marked on this chartlet are covered in greater detail in the "Ports and Approaches" section of "The Yachtsman's Manual of Tides".

Timing of passages calls for careful judgement, with due allowance for wind and weather. If the yacht will achieve about 5 knots, then the suggestions below are offered as a guide. Space is provided for adding further notes, in the light of experience with a particular yacht.

SUGGESTIONS FOR THIS TIME
Latest departure St Peter Port for St Helier
....
....
....
....

+6

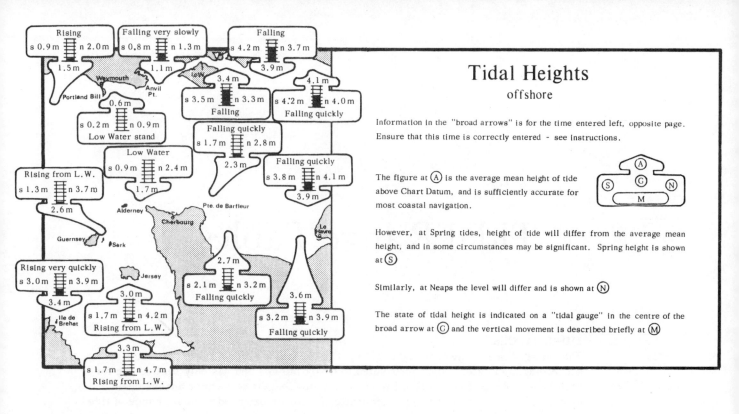

Tidal Heights
offshore

Information in the "broad arrows" is for the time entered left, opposite page. Ensure that this time is correctly entered - see instructions.

The figure at (A) is the average mean height of tide above Chart Datum, and is sufficiently accurate for most coastal navigation.

However, at Spring tides, height of tide will differ from the average mean height, and in some circumstances may be significant. Spring height is shown at (S)

Similarly, at Neaps the level will differ and is shown at (N)

The state of tidal height is indicated on a "tidal gauge" in the centre of the broad arrow at (G) and the vertical movement is described briefly at (M)

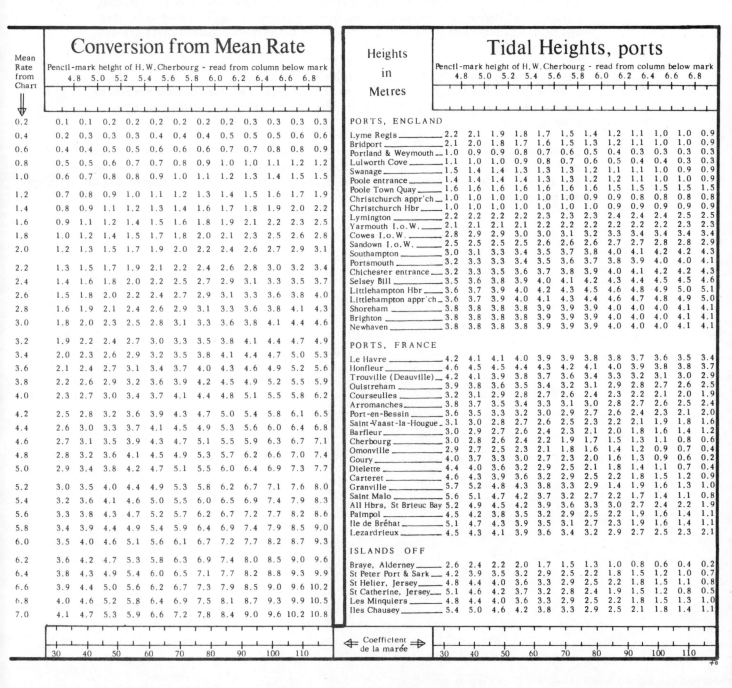

Conversion from Mean Rate

Pencil-mark height of H.W. Cherbourg - read from column below mark

Mean Rate from Chart	4.8	5.0	5.2	5.4	5.6	5.8	6.0	6.2	6.4	6.6	6.8	7.0
0.2	0.1	0.1	0.2	0.2	0.2	0.2	0.2	0.2	0.3	0.3	0.3	0.3
0.4	0.2	0.3	0.3	0.3	0.4	0.4	0.4	0.5	0.5	0.5	0.6	0.6
0.6	0.4	0.4	0.5	0.5	0.6	0.6	0.6	0.7	0.7	0.8	0.8	0.9
0.8	0.5	0.5	0.6	0.7	0.7	0.8	0.9	1.0	1.0	1.1	1.2	1.2
1.0	0.6	0.7	0.8	0.8	0.9	1.0	1.1	1.2	1.3	1.4	1.5	1.5
1.2	0.7	0.8	0.9	1.0	1.1	1.2	1.3	1.4	1.5	1.6	1.7	1.9
1.4	0.8	0.9	1.1	1.2	1.3	1.4	1.6	1.7	1.8	1.9	2.0	2.2
1.6	0.9	1.1	1.2	1.4	1.5	1.6	1.8	1.9	2.1	2.2	2.3	2.5
1.8	1.0	1.2	1.4	1.5	1.7	1.8	2.0	2.1	2.3	2.5	2.6	2.8
2.0	1.2	1.3	1.5	1.7	1.9	2.0	2.2	2.4	2.6	2.7	2.9	3.1
2.2	1.3	1.5	1.7	1.9	2.1	2.2	2.4	2.6	2.8	3.0	3.2	3.4
2.4	1.4	1.6	1.8	2.0	2.2	2.5	2.7	2.9	3.1	3.3	3.5	3.7
2.6	1.5	1.8	2.0	2.2	2.4	2.7	2.9	3.1	3.3	3.6	3.8	4.0
2.8	1.6	1.9	2.1	2.4	2.6	2.9	3.1	3.3	3.6	3.8	4.1	4.3
3.0	1.8	2.0	2.3	2.5	2.8	3.1	3.3	3.6	3.8	4.1	4.4	4.6
3.2	1.9	2.2	2.4	2.7	3.0	3.3	3.5	3.8	4.1	4.4	4.7	4.9
3.4	2.0	2.3	2.6	2.9	3.2	3.5	3.8	4.1	4.4	4.7	5.0	5.3
3.6	2.1	2.4	2.7	3.1	3.4	3.7	4.0	4.3	4.6	4.9	5.2	5.6
3.8	2.2	2.6	2.9	3.2	3.6	3.9	4.2	4.5	4.9	5.2	5.5	5.9
4.0	2.3	2.7	3.0	3.4	3.7	4.1	4.4	4.8	5.1	5.5	5.8	6.2
4.2	2.5	2.8	3.2	3.6	3.9	4.3	4.7	5.0	5.4	5.8	6.1	6.5
4.4	2.6	3.0	3.3	3.7	4.1	4.5	4.9	5.3	5.6	6.0	6.4	6.8
4.6	2.7	3.1	3.5	3.9	4.3	4.7	5.1	5.5	5.9	6.3	6.7	7.1
4.8	2.8	3.2	3.6	4.1	4.5	4.9	5.3	5.7	6.2	6.6	7.0	7.4
5.0	2.9	3.4	3.8	4.2	4.7	5.1	5.5	6.0	6.4	6.9	7.3	7.7
5.2	3.0	3.5	4.0	4.4	4.9	5.3	5.8	6.2	6.7	7.1	7.6	8.0
5.4	3.2	3.6	4.1	4.6	5.0	5.5	6.0	6.5	6.9	7.4	7.9	8.3
5.6	3.3	3.8	4.3	4.7	5.2	5.7	6.2	6.7	7.2	7.7	8.2	8.6
5.8	3.4	3.9	4.4	4.9	5.4	5.9	6.4	6.9	7.4	7.9	8.5	9.0
6.0	3.5	4.0	4.6	5.1	5.6	6.1	6.7	7.2	7.7	8.2	8.7	9.3
6.2	3.6	4.2	4.7	5.3	5.8	6.3	6.9	7.4	8.0	8.5	9.0	9.6
6.4	3.8	4.3	4.9	5.4	6.0	6.5	7.1	7.7	8.2	8.8	9.3	9.9
6.6	3.9	4.4	5.0	5.6	6.2	6.7	7.3	7.9	8.5	9.0	9.6	10.2
6.8	4.0	4.6	5.2	5.8	6.4	6.9	7.5	8.1	8.7	9.3	9.9	10.5
7.0	4.1	4.7	5.3	5.9	6.6	7.2	7.8	8.4	9.0	9.6	10.2	10.8

Coefficient de la marée: 30 40 50 60 70 80 90 100 110

Tidal Heights, ports

Heights in Metres

Pencil-mark height of H.W. Cherbourg - read from column below mark

Port	4.8	5.0	5.2	5.4	5.6	5.8	6.0	6.2	6.4	6.6	6.8	7.0
PORTS, ENGLAND												
Lyme Regis	2.2	2.1	1.9	1.8	1.7	1.5	1.4	1.2	1.1	1.0	1.0	0.9
Bridport	2.1	2.0	1.8	1.7	1.6	1.5	1.3	1.2	1.1	1.0	1.0	0.9
Portland & Weymouth	1.0	0.9	0.9	0.8	0.7	0.6	0.5	0.4	0.3	0.3	0.3	0.3
Lulworth Cove	1.1	1.0	1.0	0.9	0.8	0.7	0.6	0.5	0.4	0.4	0.3	0.3
Swanage	1.5	1.4	1.4	1.3	1.3	1.3	1.2	1.1	1.1	1.0	0.9	0.9
Poole entrance	1.4	1.4	1.4	1.4	1.3	1.3	1.2	1.1	1.1	1.0	1.0	0.9
Poole Town Quay	1.6	1.6	1.6	1.6	1.6	1.6	1.6	1.5	1.5	1.5	1.5	1.5
Christchurch appr'ch	1.0	1.0	1.0	1.0	1.0	1.0	0.9	0.9	0.8	0.8	0.8	0.8
Christchurch Hbr	1.0	1.0	1.0	1.0	1.0	1.0	1.0	0.9	0.9	0.9	0.9	0.9
Lymington	2.2	2.2	2.2	2.2	2.3	2.3	2.3	2.4	2.4	2.4	2.5	2.5
Yarmouth I.o.W.	2.1	2.1	2.1	2.1	2.2	2.2	2.2	2.2	2.2	2.2	2.3	2.3
Cowes I.o.W.	2.8	2.9	2.9	3.0	3.0	3.1	3.2	3.3	3.4	3.4	3.4	3.4
Sandown I.o.W.	2.5	2.5	2.5	2.5	2.6	2.6	2.6	2.7	2.7	2.8	2.8	2.9
Southampton	3.0	3.1	3.3	3.4	3.5	3.7	3.8	4.0	4.1	4.2	4.2	4.3
Portsmouth	3.2	3.3	3.3	3.4	3.5	3.6	3.7	3.8	3.9	4.0	4.0	4.1
Chichester entrance	3.2	3.3	3.5	3.6	3.7	3.8	3.9	4.0	4.1	4.2	4.2	4.3
Selsey Bill	3.5	3.6	3.8	3.9	4.0	4.1	4.2	4.3	4.4	4.5	4.5	4.6
Littlehampton Hbr	3.6	3.7	3.9	4.0	4.2	4.3	4.5	4.6	4.8	4.9	5.0	5.1
Littlehampton appr'ch	3.6	3.7	3.9	4.0	4.1	4.3	4.4	4.6	4.7	4.8	4.9	5.0
Shoreham	3.8	3.8	3.8	3.8	3.9	3.9	3.9	4.0	4.0	4.0	4.1	4.1
Brighton	3.8	3.8	3.8	3.8	3.9	3.9	3.9	4.0	4.0	4.0	4.1	4.1
Newhaven	3.8	3.8	3.8	3.8	3.9	3.9	3.9	4.0	4.0	4.0	4.1	4.1
PORTS, FRANCE												
Le Havre	4.2	4.1	4.1	4.0	3.9	3.9	3.8	3.8	3.7	3.6	3.5	3.4
Honfleur	4.6	4.5	4.5	4.4	4.3	4.2	4.1	4.0	3.9	3.8	3.8	3.7
Trouville (Deauville)	4.2	4.1	3.9	3.8	3.7	3.6	3.4	3.3	3.2	3.1	3.0	2.9
Oulstreham	3.9	3.8	3.6	3.5	3.4	3.2	3.1	2.9	2.8	2.7	2.6	2.5
Courseulles	3.2	3.1	2.9	2.8	2.7	2.6	2.4	2.3	2.2	2.1	2.0	1.9
Arromanches	3.8	3.7	3.5	3.4	3.3	3.1	3.0	2.8	2.7	2.6	2.5	2.4
Port-en-Bessin	3.6	3.5	3.3	3.2	3.0	2.9	2.7	2.6	2.4	2.3	2.1	2.0
Saint-Vaast-la-Hougue	3.1	3.0	2.8	2.7	2.6	2.5	2.3	2.2	2.1	1.9	1.8	1.6
Barfleur	3.0	2.9	2.7	2.6	2.4	2.3	2.1	2.0	1.8	1.6	1.4	1.2
Cherbourg	3.0	2.8	2.6	2.4	2.2	1.9	1.7	1.5	1.3	1.1	0.8	0.6
Omonville	2.9	2.7	2.5	2.3	2.1	1.8	1.6	1.4	1.2	0.9	0.7	0.4
Goury	4.0	3.7	3.3	3.0	2.7	2.3	2.0	1.6	1.3	0.9	0.6	0.2
Dielette	4.4	4.0	3.6	3.2	2.9	2.5	2.1	1.8	1.4	1.1	0.7	0.4
Carteret	4.6	4.3	3.9	3.6	3.2	2.9	2.5	2.2	1.8	1.5	1.2	0.9
Granville	5.7	5.2	4.8	4.3	3.8	3.3	2.9	2.4	1.9	1.6	1.3	1.0
Saint Malo	5.6	5.1	4.7	4.2	3.7	3.2	2.7	2.2	1.7	1.4	1.1	0.8
All Hbrs, St Brieuc Bay	5.2	4.9	4.5	4.2	3.9	3.6	3.3	3.0	2.7	2.4	2.2	1.9
Paimpol	4.5	4.2	3.8	3.5	3.2	2.9	2.5	2.2	1.9	1.6	1.4	1.1
Ile de Bréhat	5.1	4.7	4.3	3.9	3.5	3.1	2.7	2.3	1.9	1.6	1.4	1.1
Lezardrieux	4.5	4.3	4.1	3.9	3.6	3.4	3.2	2.9	2.7	2.3	2.3	2.1
ISLANDS OFF												
Braye, Alderney	2.6	2.4	2.2	2.0	1.7	1.5	1.3	1.0	0.8	0.6	0.4	0.2
St Peter Port & Sark	4.2	3.9	3.5	3.2	2.9	2.5	2.2	1.8	1.5	1.2	1.0	0.7
St Helier, Jersey	4.8	4.4	4.0	3.6	3.3	2.9	2.5	2.2	1.8	1.5	1.1	0.8
St Catherine, Jersey	5.1	4.6	4.2	3.7	3.2	2.8	2.4	1.9	1.5	1.2	0.8	0.5
Les Minquiers	4.8	4.4	4.0	3.6	3.3	2.9	2.5	2.2	1.8	1.5	1.3	1.0
Iles Chausey	5.4	5.0	4.6	4.2	3.8	3.3	2.9	2.5	2.1	1.8	1.4	1.1

Coefficient de la marée: 30 40 50 60 70 80 90 100 110

Tidal Range Tables

TIDAL RANGES

The range of tide is the difference in height between low water and the preceding or succeeding high water. It is not related to Chart Datum, and has only limited use for yachtsmen. Range can be helpful when calculating lengths of warp or anchor chain, especially when a yacht has to be left unattended for an extended period. Range of tide is also needed for computing the rates of streams when using Admiralty tidal stream atlases, and although the figures provided in these tables are approximate only, they will be adequate for this purpose if tide tables for the various Standard Ports are not carried aboard.

INSTRUCTIONS FOR THE USE OF TIDAL RANGE TABLES

1 From Cherbourg tide tables extract the height of high water for the time nearest to that for which the information is required. Pencil-mark the scale at the top of the table against this height.

2 Enter the table with the port or place for which the tidal range is required, and read from the column under the pencil-mark. If the pencil-mark falls between two columns, then interpolate between the columns. The figure thus extracted is the range of tide in that place for that particular tide.

Tidal Ranges in metres

Pencil-mark height of H.W.Cherbourg - read from column below mark

Port		4.8	5.0	5.2	5.4	5.6	5.8	6.0	6.2	6.4	6.6	6.8
PORTS, ENGLAND												
Lyme Regis	0.9	1.2	1.6	1.9	2.3	2.6	3.0	3.3	3.7	3.9	4.2	4.4
Bridport	0.9	1.2	1.6	1.9	2.2	2.5	2.9	3.2	3.5	3.8	4.0	4.3
Portland & Weymouth	0.4	0.6	0.8	1.0	1.2	1.3	1.5	1.7	1.9	2.1	2.2	2.4
Lulworth Cove	0.3	0.5	0.7	0.9	1.1	1.4	1.6	1.8	2.0	2.2	2.4	2.6
Swanage	0.3	0.4	0.6	0.7	0.8	0.9	1.0	1.3	1.5	1.7	1.8	2.0
Poole entrance	0.4	0.5	0.5	0.6	0.6	0.7	1.0	1.2	1.5	1.7	1.8	2.0
Poole Town Quay	0.5	0.6	0.6	0.7	0.8	0.9	1.2	1.4	1.7	1.8	2.0	2.2
Christchurch appr'ch	0.5	0.6	0.6	0.7	0.8	0.9	1.2	1.6	1.9	2.0	2.1	2.2
Christchurch Hbr	0.6	0.7	0.7	0.8	0.8	0.9	1.1	1.2	1.4	1.5	1.5	1.6
Lymington	0.6	0.8	1.0	1.2	1.5	1.7	1.9	2.1	2.3	2.5	2.6	2.8
Yarmouth I.o.W.	0.8	0.9	1.1	1.2	1.4	1.5	1.7	1.9	2.1	2.3	2.6	2.8
Cowes I.o.W.	1.2	1.5	1.7	2.0	2.2	2.5	2.8	3.1	3.4	3.6	3.9	4.1
Sandown I.o.W.	1.0	1.3	1.5	1.8	2.1	2.4	2.7	2.9	3.2	3.5	3.8	4.1
Southampton	1.4	1.7	2.1	2.4	2.7	3.0	3.4	3.7	4.0	4.2	4.4	4.6
Portsmouth	1.5	1.8	2.2	2.5	2.8	3.1	3.5	3.8	4.1	4.3	4.4	4.6
Chichester entrance	1.7	2.0	2.4	2.7	3.0	3.3	3.6	3.9	4.2	4.4	4.4	4.8
Selsey Bill	2.1	2.4	2.8	3.1	3.4	3.7	4.1	4.4	4.7	4.9	5.1	5.3
Littlehampton Hbr	2.2	2.5	2.9	3.2	3.5	3.8	4.2	4.5	4.8	5.0	5.2	5.4
Littlehampton appr'ch	2.4	2.7	3.1	3.4	3.8	4.1	4.5	4.8	5.2	5.4	5.7	5.9
Shoreham	2.5	2.9	3.3	3.7	4.0	4.4	4.8	5.1	5.5	5.8	6.0	6.3
Brighton	2.6	3.0	3.4	3.8	4.2	4.7	5.1	5.5	5.9	6.2	6.5	6.8
Newhaven	2.7	3.1	3.5	3.9	4.4	4.8	5.2	5.7	6.1	6.4	6.7	7.0
PORTS, FRANCE												
Le Havre	2.9	3.4	3.8	4.3	4.8	5.2	5.7	6.1	6.6	7.0	7.3	7.7
Honfleur	3.2	3.6	4.0	4.4	4.9	5.3	5.7	6.2	6.6	6.9	7.2	7.5
Trouville (Deauville)	2.9	3.4	3.8	4.3	4.8	5.3	5.7	6.2	6.7	7.0	7.4	7.7
Ouistreham	2.9	3.4	3.8	4.3	4.8	5.3	5.7	6.2	6.7	7.0	7.4	7.7
Courseulles	2.6	3.1	3.6	4.0	4.4	4.9	5.3	5.8	6.2	6.5	6.9	7.2
Arromanches	2.6	3.1	3.5	4.0	4.5	4.9	5.4	5.8	6.3	6.6	7.0	7.3
Port-en-Bessin	2.7	3.1	3.5	3.9	4.4	4.8	5.2	5.7	6.1	6.4	6.8	7.1
Saint-Vaast-la-Hougue	2.5	2.9	3.3	3.7	4.1	4.5	4.9	5.3	5.7	6.2	6.6	7.1
Barfleur	2.2	2.6	3.0	3.4	3.8	4.2	4.6	5.0	5.4	5.8	6.3	6.7
Cherbourg	1.9	2.3	2.7	3.1	3.5	4.0	4.4	4.8	5.2	5.7	6.1	6.6
Omonville	1.8	2.2	2.6	3.0	3.4	3.9	4.3	4.7	5.1	5.6	6.1	6.6
Goury	2.4	2.9	3.5	4.0	4.5	5.1	5.6	6.2	6.7	7.2	7.8	8.3
Dielette	2.6	3.3	4.1	4.8	5.5	6.2	7.0	7.7	8.4	9.0	9.6	10.2
Carteret	3.2	4.0	4.8	5.6	6.4	7.2	8.0	8.8	9.6	10.2	10.9	11.5
Granville	3.6	4.6	5.6	6.6	7.6	8.6	9.6	10.6	11.6	12.3	13.0	13.7
Saint Malo	3.4	4.3	5.3	6.2	7.1	8.0	9.0	9.9	10.8	11.5	12.1	12.8
All Hbrs, St Brieuc Bay	3.2	4.1	4.9	5.8	6.6	7.5	8.3	9.2	10.0	10.6	11.2	11.8
Paimpol	3.4	4.2	5.0	5.8	6.6	7.5	8.3	9.1	9.9	10.6	11.2	11.9
Ile de Bréhat	3.3	4.0	4.8	5.5	6.2	7.0	7.7	8.5	9.2	9.8	10.4	11.0
Lezardrieux	3.4	4.1	4.9	5.6	6.4	7.1	7.9	8.6	9.4	10.0	10.6	11.1
ISLANDS OFF												
Braye, Alderney	1.8	2.3	2.7	3.2	3.7	4.1	4.6	5.0	5.5	5.9	6.4	6.8
St Peter Port & Sark	2.1	2.8	3.6	4.3	5.0	5.8	6.5	7.3	8.0	8.6	9.1	9.7
St Helier, Jersey	2.7	3.6	4.4	5.3	6.2	7.1	8.0	8.9	9.8	10.5	11.2	11.9
St Catherine, Jersey	2.4	3.3	4.3	5.2	6.1	7.0	8.0	9.0	9.9	10.4	11.4	12.1
Les Minquiers	3.8	4.6	5.4	6.2	7.0	7.8	8.6	9.4	10.2	10.8	11.4	12.0
Iles Chausey	4.0	4.9	5.7	6.6	7.5	8.4	9.3	10.2	11.1	11.8	12.5	13.2

Coefficient de la marée: 30 40 50 60 70 80 90 100 110

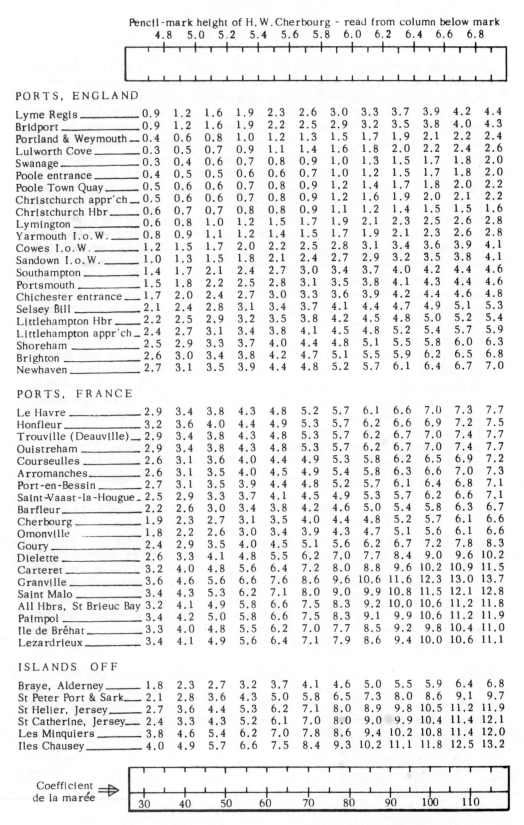

Caution: Ranges are not related to Chart Datum

Dipping Distances

It is in the approach to a landfall that the yachtsman will often have moments of worry and doubt, and it is at these times, given adequate visibility, that lights and dipping distances are extremely valuable aids to navigation. When a light first appears over the horizon, not only can a bearing be taken and a position line drawn on the chart, but its distance from the observer can be simply calculated as a dipping distance and thus provide a splendid fix. The diagram opposite illustrates the way in which the curvature of the earth affects the distance at which lights are visible. From the diagram it will be obvious that the higher the light the further off it can be seen - always provided that the light exhibited is bright enough and that it is not so high as to be obscured by low cloud. It will further be obvious that as a vessel approaches a lighthouse the light will quite suddenly appear on the horizon, and as it moves away from a lighthouse the light will just as suddenly disappear below the horizon. The point at which the light appears or disappears is the dipping distance. Heights of terrestial objects such as lighthouses, hilltops and headlands are marked on modern charts in metres and on fathoms charts in feet above the level of Mean High Water Springs, and these heights are an essential factor in determining the distance between the observer aboard a yacht and the object. If the heights of lights are not marked on the chart, then the Admiralty List of Lights or one of the popular almanacs should be consulted - and this is always best done at the passage planning stage. Tides also play a part in the calculations because as the tide falls from the level of M.H.W.S. the yacht falls with it, and the observed terrestial object increases its apparent height. Thus a lighthouse may exhibit a light 20 metres above sea level at high water springs, but be 30 metres above sea level at low water 6 hours later. By referring to the diagram we see that at high water this light will dip when about $12\frac{1}{2}$ miles distant, but dip at $14\frac{1}{2}$ miles at low water. Note that the effect of tides on dipping distances is greater for lights exhibited at low elevations.

Exposed Heights   When sailing in areas where tidal ranges are considerable it will be necessary to take into account any 'exposed height' - that is, the additional height caused by the fall of tide from the level of M.H.W.S. This can be found by referring to the 'Tidal Heights Offshore' chartlets in the Tidal Atlas where the height for every hour of the tidal cycle is shown in the 'broad arrows'. This figure is subtracted from the Spring figure in the same position on the chartlet where the broad arrow indicates High Water, thus determining the exposed height. This must be added to the height of the light as shown on the chart, and the adjusted height applied to the diagram opposite to determine the dipping distance.

Observer's Eye Level   The diagram opposite supposes that the yachtsman's eye is 2 metres above sea level. Since most cruising yachts have their cockpit soles a few inches above sea level a standing watchkeeper should have his line of sight at approximately the right height; on larger yachts a sitting position could be adopted.